RADICAL MATH

MILLENNIUM EDITION

VOLUME X

CARD & DICE GAMES FOR GRADES 6 TO 12

The authors would like to thank Cheri Eck, Nancy McGuire and Linda Williams for their game creations.

The games contributed by our consultants will be indicated under the title of the game.

Written by:

Joanne Currah
Jane Felling

2nd Printing November 2004

"Box Cars" won the National Learning Disabilities Association Idea of the Year 1991.

For Our Wonderful
Families who have guided
us through our books.

With our love and thanks,

Joanne and Jane

TABLE OF CONTENTS

Back To Basics

Back To Basics (continued)

Order Of Operations

Exponents and Radicals

Polynomials And Their Operations

Linear Equations

Coordinate Geometry

Probability

Fractions and Ratios

Fractions and Ratios (continued)

Mixed Bag

Dear MRS. CURRAH & MRS. Felling,

Krysty !

Matt

Dani!

Hope you know
how very much
you're appreciated.

Thank you so much
for all your "Math
Help" – we are truly
enjoying your visits!! See
you soon! Michelle
Morrissette

Thanks For the Fun Games!!

FROM, All of US in Grade 7.!

Breanna

Ashley

Geoff

Krystina
Wincentaylo

Micki

Katlan

CHRIS

Oh Hello

Katelyn P.

Con

Amanda

mike A.

KURT

Paul

JustinB.

(A
:
X

Elysia

Justin R.

Kimberly

Kacie

INTRODUCTION

It has been five years since our first book was published specifically targeting the Grade 7 - 12 level.

Over this period we have met hundreds of teachers at conferences and in our workshops who have provided us with invaluable feedback and constructive suggestions on how we could better reach this level of student.

Rather than edit and reprint our original Radical Math we decided to create a completely new Radical Math - Millennium Edition. A book that would fill in our "missing gaps". While working with the higher grades we became aware of the curriculum areas that we hadn't fully covered and hence, a new Grade 6 - 12 book was soon in the works!

The games contained in our newest volume use regular and multi-sided dice, as well as ordinary playing cards. Some absolute favourites have been kept in this volume but there are over sixty new games.

We feel confident that Radical Math for the Millennium will challenge your students and create unique opportunities for you to explore math in a fascinating and exciting way.

HAVE FUN AND GET RADICAL!

Joanne and Jane

THE BOX CARS AND ONE-EYED JACKS PHILOSOPHY

The Box Cars and One-Eyed Jacks series of books promote the use of games using cards, dice and multi-sided dice to teach mathematics. Starting with a very simple concept ten years ago, the series has evolved to encompass much more than "having fun with games" to practice basic and advanced mathematical concepts.

From day one, we had a strong vision about children learning through games. After ten years we are continuing to work towards our vision but are now able to express it more clearly. We've learned, and are continuing to learn about why games work.

1. Students are naturally intrigued and captivated by math games. Whether a game is simple or complex, the highly motivating materials of cards, dice and multi-sided dice attract and hold a learner's attention.

2. Games fit the research that indicates brief, engaging, purposeful practice is a powerful strategy for developing understanding and mastery of basic concepts. Games can be easily changed and manipulated to suit the needs of the learner and the teaching objective. All students play, but with many variations students are able to respond at different levels and in different ways to an activity.

3. Games allow students to work in a non-threatening atmosphere towards mastery of concepts. When motivating, challenging, problem solving activities are integrated into games, students are able to learn as they are developmentally ready. By using games, teachers can capitalize on students' innate desire to play and learn through play. If the atmosphere is positive and flexible, students are more likely to learn.

4. Games can engage learners in a cycle of mathematical thinking. As they play a math game students:

    a) formulate questions.

    b) create strategies.

    c) will often use an unsophisticated "it seems to work" method. Success is a result of experimenting with this trial and error approach.

    d) adopt a strategy for methods that work consistently over time.

This type of activity requires the learner to use critical thinking and logical reasoning as they analyze and become aware of their strategies. Making sense of mathematical ideas, acquiring skills and solving problems is at the very heart of mathematics. Good thought provoking games allow students the opportunity to get there.

5. Games can provide an excellent experience for learners to write about mathematics and their learning. As they develop and analyze their strategies they must clarify their thinking in order to share their ideas with others. Writing responses to game activities helps many students reach this understanding and apply reasoning processes to similar situations. The learner realizes the value of these experiences as they can transfer their knowledge to other related experiences. As students play they naturally converse. There are ample opportunities for teachers to informally assess a student's understanding by "playing alongside", observing, or having them demonstrate the game. This first hand assessment leads to further instruction.

6. Our math games are multi-sensory and accommodate all learning styles. The cards and dice are tactile and are used as true math manipulatives. Cards and dice are extremely visual with predictable patterns. Learners constantly "talk the math" as they play and/or re-teach, making games auditory, and socially interactive in nature. For some students, the physical component of active learning is key to transferring their knowledge to other related experiences (i.e. real-life situations).

In conclusion,

If math is a game, then respect and challenge its power and potential as a teaching strategy for effective learning!

Roll the dice, deal the cards and get playing. Everybody WINS!

HOW TO USE THIS BOOK

Radical Math Volume X - Millennium Edition contains 103 games and is divided into nine sections.

1. Back to Basics

2. Order of Operations

3. Exponents and Radicals

4. Polynomials and their Operations

5. Linear Equations

6. Coordinate Geometry

7. Probability

8. Fractions and Ratios

9. Mixed Bag

Within each section the games are organized using the following format:

LEVEL: This is the appropriate grade level (suggested only). It is intended to be flexible.

SKILLS: Specific math skills are listed here.

EQUIPMENT: Specific items are listed including which card values are needed. An ace is given the value of 1 in all of our games - indicated (Ace = 1) in the instructions. We use the Kings as 0's. If a reproducible is needed it will be indicated in the rules and found at the back of the book. Keep in mind that students may be able to simply copy the gameboard in their Box Cars book or math book to save on photocopying.

GETTING STARTED: These are the rules and instructions which can be changed to meet the various levels within the class-room.

VARIATIONS: Variations are ideas to increase or decrease difficulty, or to extend the concept and add new skills.

TEACHING TIPS, THOUGHT PROVOKERS and RADICAL RULES:

The Teaching Tips will provide specific suggestions for teaching a strategy or concept within the context of that game. It is advisable to read through the entire game prior to playing, as in some instances the Teaching Tips are best shared before the game is introduced.

THOUGHT PROVOKER GAMES

We selected what we considered to be our best games where the "play" experience can lead to excellent mathematical extensions and writing opportunities. Students should be allowed "more than a one shot play" of the game. We suggest the following format for Thought Provoker Games.

1) Day One of the Game: 45 - 60 minutes are necessary to introduce the game rules and allow for a sufficient play period. If the game includes Thought Provokers, these should be read and discussed prior to playing. During the last 15 minutes, have students share their developing strategies in a guided discussion.

2) Throughout the week, allow students to have follow up play periods during free time (this could even be at recess or break time: approximately 20 minutes). Encourage and organize opportunities for students to play the games at home. Having students re-teach the game rules to other family members or each other is very effective for reinforcing concepts.

3) The following week, lead a class discussion about the game. Have students share their responses and strategies. Allow time for students to follow up and write their responses to the Thought Provokers (if this was not completed during the week).

It is our experience that encouraging children to verbalize their ideas to others enhances their written work and understanding. Communicating their strategies and experiences helps to clarify what they put down on paper. Build in sharing time in the math class to maximize success in writing the Thought Provokers. Knowing ahead of time what they will be writing about helps focus their play. We tell them it gets their "brains ready to look for and experience the math they have to write about". Providing the questions ahead of time also allows the teacher to focus their own observations as they circulate in the classroom. We will often catch students verbalizing answers to some of the questions and we reinforce this learning by confirming, "You're on the right track."

$\sqrt{\text{RADICAL RULES:}}$

Radical Rules are inserted throughout the book. These are excellent mathematical explanations, connections and teaching strategies for specific concepts connected to the games. They can be copied and used with both students and parents.

The games do not have to be played in any set order. Teachers and parents can select games to introduce a concept or skill, practice a concept or skill (see Math Warm-Ups section) or master a concept or skill.

The rules and instructions for all games are meant to be flexible. We encourage you and your students to change the equipment, skills or rules. As you play more of the games, you will discover how easy it is to change and re-invent during the game playing process.

Back To Basics

DO YOUR DECIMALS

LEVEL: Grade 6 and up

SKILLS: Adding whole numbers and decimals, place value

PLAYERS: 4 (2 vs. 2) or 2 (1 vs. 1)

EQUIPMENT: Cards King - 9 (King = 0, Ace = 1), paper, pencil

GETTING STARTED: Player One turns over three cards and makes a three-digit number, with black cards as whole numbers and red cards as decimals. Player One turns over three more cards and adds the second number to the first.

EXAMPLE I:

Player One: black 4, red 1, red 6:   4.16

            red 3, black 2, black 1: <u>21.3</u>

                                    25.46

Player Two now takes their turn and both players continue keeping a tally of their scores until one player is the closest to 1 000 without exceeding it. If a player builds a number that, when added, is greater than 1 000, this player 'strikes out' for that round.

EXAMPLE II:

Player One only:

1. black 6, black 2, red 5:   62.5
   black 1, red 6, red 8:   <u>+ 1.68</u>
                          64.18

2. red 7, red 3, red 1:   .731
   black 2, red 1, black 9: <u>+ 92.1</u>
                          92.831

                        64.18
                    <u>+ 92.831</u>
                  157.011   etc.

VARIATION: Players multiply their numbers instead of adding.

VARIATION II: Least sum wins.

√ RADICAL RULES: To add or subtract decimals, place the numbers in a column with the decimal points lined up. Add or subtract just as you would for whole numbers. Line up the decimal points in the result under the decimal points in the column.

OPERATION DECIMAL

LEVEL: Grade 6 and up

SKILLS: Multiplying whole numbers and decimals

PLAYERS: 4 (2 vs. 2) or 2 (1 vs. 1)

EQUIPMENT: Cards Ace - 10 (Ace = 1), one ten-sided (0-9) die, paper, pencil

GETTING STARTED: Each player takes two cards and makes a two-digit number (black cards are whole numbers, red cards are decimals). The die is rolled and players each multiply their number by the roll of the die. Players record their products on a tally sheet. After ten rounds, each player or team adds all of their products together. The greatest accumulated sum wins the game.

EXAMPLE I:

Player One	Player Two
red 5, black 8 = 8.5	red 10, black 4 = 4.10

die roll = 4

8.5 x 4 = 34.0	4.10 x 4 = 16.4

VARIATION: Players take three cards, build their number, and multiply this number by the die roll, or take four numbers and multiply two, two-digit numbers.

EXAMPLE II:

Player One	Player Two
black 7, black 4, red 3 = 47.3	red 6, black 5, red 2 = 5.62

die roll: 8

47.3 x 8 = 378.4	5.62 x 8 = 44.96

√ RADICAL RULES: Multiply decimals just as you would whole numbers. Then in the product, beginning at the right, count off as many decimal places as there are in the multiplier and in the multiplicand together. Then place the decimal point that many places in.

$$\begin{array}{r} .42 \\ \underline{\times\ .2} \\ .084 \end{array}$$

(3 decimal places in all) A zero needs to go before the two digits in the product to equal three place holders.

18

DECIMAL DANCE

LEVEL: Grade 6 and up

SKILLS: Reading decimals

PLAYERS: 2

EQUIPMENT: Regular dice, cards Ace - 9 (Ace = 1) in one pile, Ace - 6 (Ace = 1) in another, counters

GETTING STARTED: Each player draws nine cards and makes a nine-digit number. The player puts down a counter (a bingo chip or other marker) as a decimal place and reads their number to their partner. The player may select any place value position to put their decimal marker.

EXAMPLE: **Player One:** 119 634.862 "one hundred nineteen thousand, six hundred thirty-four and (decimal) eight hundred, sixty-two thousandths."

Player Two: 54 315 693.7 "fifty-four million, three hundred fifteen thousand, six hundred ninety-three and (decimal) seven tenths."

Player One rolls a die to determine who wins the point. An odd roll (1, 3, or 5) means that the least number wins the point, while an even roll (2, 4, or 6) means that the greatest number wins. Players continue to turn cards over and arrange them. The first player to score 20 points is the winner.

√RADICAL RULES: The word decimal means relating to the number 10. In our decimal system, each place has ten times the value of the place to its right. When reading decimals, read the whole number part first. Then say the decimal point as "and". Continue reading the rest of the digits just as if it were a whole number as well as reading the place value of the last digit.

e.g.   3.465

say: "three and four hundred sixty-five thousandths"

WHAT'S YOUR NUMBER?

LEVEL: Grade 6 - 9

SKILLS: Place value to 100 000 000, probability

PLAYERS: 2 - 4 or teacher vs. whole class

EQUIPMENT: One ten-sided (0-9) die, paper, pencil

GETTING STARTED: The goal of the game is to create the largest number possible. One player is selected to be the roller for the round. Each player creates their gameboard as follows:

Hundred Millions 100 000 000	Ten Millions 10 000 000	Millions 1 000 000	Hundred Thousands 100 000	Ten Thousands 10 000	Thousands 1 000	Hundreds 100	Tens 10	Ones 1

The selected player begins by rolling the die. All players must write this number down and may choose any place value position on their gameboard. Numbers cannot be erased once placed.

Play continues by rolling out eight more numbers to complete the round. When all spaces are filled in, players compare numbers. The player(s) with the greatest number scores 1 point.

A new round begins by selecting a new roller. Play continues for a set period of time. The player with the most points is the winner.

THOUGHT PROVOKERS:

Have students play ten rounds with a 100 000 000 gameboard. Answer the following questions:

1. After ten rounds you will have rolled 90 times. Graph how many times you rolled each number. Were the rolls evenly distributed? Explain.

2. Record the greatest possible number that could have been rolled for each round. Use a calculator to figure out the difference between the number you built and the greatest possible. Figure out your average difference.

Your Number	Greatest Possible	Difference

3. What is the greatest possible number that could be rolled? Could this, or would this ever happen? Explain.

4. Expand all the numbers you made.

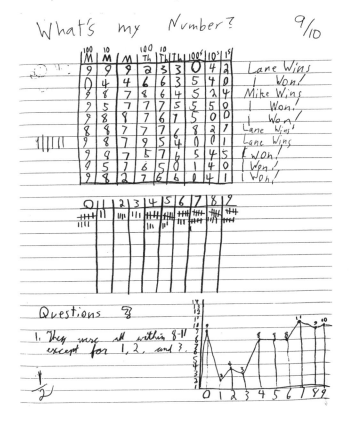

What's my Number?   9/10

$$\begin{array}{r} 999977762 \\ 887276829 \\ \hline 1\,01\,100533 \end{array}$$

2.

My Number	Greatest Possible	Difference
999233042	999433220	200178
044663540	665444300	620780760
987864524	988765442	900918
957775550	977755550	19980000
988767500	988776500	9000
887776829	988877762	101100933
987954001	998754100	10800099
987576545	987765554	189009
957650140	975554100	18903960
982766041	987664210	4898169

3. 999 999 999 × Yes but but highly unlikely

Skills Required : Counting   * 1 per game or
                 Addition *   none per game
                 Subtraction *
                 Multiplication *

# of players: 2-4   3/5

EXPANDER

LEVEL:	Grade 6 - 9
SKILLS:	Expanding numbers, adding to 100 000
PLAYERS:	Small groups, or teacher vs. whole class
EQUIPMENT:	One twenty-sided (1-20) die, pencil, paper
GETTING STARTED:	The goal of the game is to create the largest number possible. The player(s) with the largest number score 1 point for that round. Groups can play to a set score (e.g. 10 or 20 points) or for a set amount of time. Each player makes a grid as follows:

Hundred Thousands	Ten Thousands	Thousands	Hundreds	Tens	Ones

One player is selected to be the roller to roll for the round. The die is rolled and each player must record that number somewhere on their grid. Players may choose any place value position on their board. Numbers cannot be erased once placed. Once all players have filled in this number, the die is rolled again. This number is also placed in the grid. Four more rolls are taken to fill the grid, for a total of six rolls.

EXAMPLE: The six rolls are 12, 14, 6, 9, 11, 5

Player One

H Th	T Th	Th	H	T	O
5	14	12	9	6	11

Player Two

H Th	T Th	Th	H	T	O
5	12	14	11	9	6

At the end of the six rolls, players total their rolls as follows:

Player One	Player Two
500 000	500 000
140 000	120 000
12 000	14 000
900	1 100
60	90
11	6
652 971	635 196

Player One scores 1 point for the round.

VARIATION: Use thirty-sided (1-30) dice and play using the same game rules.

THOUGHT PROVOKERS:

1. Record the greatest possible number that could have been rolled for each round. Use a calculator to figure out the difference between the number you built and the greatest possible. Figure out your average difference.

Your Number	Greatest Possible	Difference

2. What is the greatest possible number that could be rolled? Could this, or would this ever happen? Explain.

DICEY DECIMALS

LEVEL: Grade 6 - 9

SKILLS: Recognizing place value from 100 000 to .000 001

PLAYERS: 2 or more

EQUIPMENT: Cards Ace - 9 (Ace = 1), regular dice, paper, pencil, markers

GETTING STARTED: The goal of the game is to be the player with the highest accumulative total. To begin, each player draws six cards and makes a six-digit number face up. Each player then rolls a die to determine where they must place a decimal point in their number. Beginning at the end of the number, counting that many place values to the left:

EXAMPLE:

Player One: 583 216   **Player Two:** 711 936
rolls 2   rolls 4
5 832.16   71.193 6
　↑   ↑

Decimal placed 2   Decimal placed 4
place values in.   place values in.

Players verbalize their numbers out loud. A die is now rolled to determine the number of points scored. The number rolled is the place value that counts for points.

EXAMPLE: Roll: 4

* Player One earns 30 points as 3 tens is in the fourth position of their number.

* Player Two earns .1 points as .1 is in the fourth position of their number.

ROLL ON... DECIMALS

(Submitted by Nancy McGuire)

LEVEL: Grade 6 - 9

SKILLS: Decimal place value, adding decimals, probability, reasoning

PLAYERS: Whole class or small group

EQUIPMENT: Two ten-sided (0-9) dice, gameboard (see reproducibles)

GETTING STARTED: The goal of the game is to add decimals to get as close to a whole number as possible. A roller is selected for the group. The dice are rolled and all players use these numbers to make a decimal number on their gameboard. Players now decide how they are going to set the numbers rolled. Players may use a 0 in combination with the rolled numbers to create any possible decimal number. For example, if a player rolls a 6 and an 8 they can create the following numbers:

.86   .68   .068   .086   .806   .608

The running total will determine the player's best choice.

e.g. Current total = .75 and player rolls 4 and 2
    It would be best to form .24 and add to equal .99
    (.01 from a whole number).

All players must construct a decimal before the next roll is made. Roller continues rolling for a total of five rolls. Players must use the numbers rolled from all five rolls.

Player closest to any whole number wins the point.

EXAMPLE:
Roll #1:   3, 4
Roll #2:   7, 0
Roll #3:   3, 1
Roll #4:   8, 9
Roll #5:   4, 0

In the event of a tie, play out a sixth roll to determine the winner.

Player One's Gameboard

Roll Number	Ones	Tenths 10ths	Hundredths 100ths	Thousandths 1000ths	Running Total
1		3	0	4	.304
2		0	7	0	+ .070 = .374
3		3	1	0	+ .310 = .684
4		0	8	9	+ .089 = .773
5		0	4	0	+ .040 = .813

(+/-) $\boxed{-.187}$

Player Two's Gameboard

Roll Number	Ones	Tenths 10ths	Hundredths 100ths	Thousandths 1000ths	Running Total
1		4	3	0	.430
2		0	0	7	+ .007 = .437
3		0	1	3	+ .013 = .450
4		0	8	9	+ .089 = .539
5		4	0	0	+ .400 = .939

(+/-) $\boxed{-.061}$

Player Two scores 1 point.

VARIATION: Subtract from one whole number to get the closest to 0.

DECI-DECA

LEVEL: Grade 6 - 9

SKILLS: Mental math, multiplying decimals and whole numbers

PLAYERS: 2

EQUIPMENT: Cards King - 9 (King = 0, Ace = 1), calculators, gameboards: A, B, or C (see reproducibles)

GETTING STARTED: The goal of the game is to create the greatest product. Before the game begins, players need to choose the same gameboard from which to play (each player needs their own board). Both players now flip a card off the top of their deck, place it into their gameboard and roll their decadie. Each player now mentally calculates their product by multiplying the cards as a decimal and the decadie as the whole number.

EXAMPLE: **Player One**

Player Two

Player Two verbalizes "32 is greater than 6" and earns Player One's card (and places it into their point pile). If a player verbalizes their product correctly without using a calculator, then they may take a <u>bonus</u> card off their card pile and place it into their point pile.

Play continues for a set period of time. The player with the most cards wins.

"This game helped me practice my mental math. In order to calculate the product, I multiplied and <u>adjusted</u> the decimal."

A TARGET ROUND

LEVEL:	Grade 6 - 9
SKILLS:	Comparing and building numbers to 9 090, rounding to the nearest thousands Variation: Comparing and building numbers to 909 090, rounding to the nearest hundred thousands.
PLAYERS:	2 - 4
EQUIPMENT:	Cards King - 9 (King = 0, Ace = 1), two or three decadice, gameboard (see reproducibles), paper, pencil
GETTING STARTED:	Play begins by rolling the two decadice and players cooperatively make a thousands number for their target (e.g. 8 010 = eight thousand ten). Players are now dealt four cards each.
	Players arrange their cards to build a number that when rounded to the nearest thousand is closest to the target.
EXAMPLE:	Player One's cards: 5, 4, 2, 0 - rounded to 5 000.
	Player Two's cards: 2, 1, 8, 7 - makes 8 172 rounded to 8 000.
	Player Two earns 1 point for being closest to the target. In the event of a tie (i.e. both players' numbers are equally close to the target) both players earn a point. The dice are re-rolled for a new target and players are dealt four new cards. Play continues for a set period of time. The player with the most points is the winner.
TEACHING TIP:	Have players record their numbers rounded to and the target number.

THOUGHT PROVOKERS:

1. Does it make any difference as to whether you make your number before or after the other players? Explain.

2. Describe the rule for rounding to a younger player. Explain any techniques you use to make rounding easier.

3. Were there any rounds where both players made rounded numbers with their cards that were equally as close to the target roll? How often did this happen?

VARIATION: For practice up to 909 090 each player is dealt six cards. At the same time, three decadice are rolled to set the target (players do this cooperatively). Players build numbers into the hundred thousands place, that when rounded to the nearest hundred thousand is closest to the target.

EXAMPLE: Target: 608 030

Player One builds 587 324 and rounds to 600 000.

Use the same Thought Provokers as in the original rules (see above).

SOMETHING TO TRY: Try playing as follows and discuss the new Thought Provokers.

Players are dealt the appropriate number of cards. They do not rearrange them. The first card is placed into the highest place value holder, the next card the second highest, etc.

EXAMPLE:

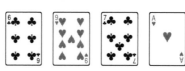

The number is then rounded to the nearest thousand (e.g. 6 971 is rounded to 7 000).

Two decadice are now rolled. The player with the rounded number closest to the target earns a point.

THOUGHT PROVOKERS:

1. How often do you think you will tie with other players?

2. If you could have rearranged your cards in this game do you think you would be more successful in being closer to the target?

ADVANCED VARIATION: We tried this in Grade 5, 6 and 7 and experienced some excellent results. Try playing as follows and discuss the accompanying Thought Provokers.

Each player is dealt six cards and players may choose to arrange them in any order. Once players freeze their numbers, they round them to the nearest 100 000.

The dice are then rolled to establish the target. Players now compare their rounded number to the target. The player with the rounded number nearest the target earns 1 point.

 **TEACHING TIP:** Players need to think about the probability of the roll over time. This will help them to develop strategy for building their numbers so they maximize their chances of scoring.

THOUGHT PROVOKERS:

1. What strategy did you use when arranging your cards when you first started playing? Did it change over time? Explain.

2. What place value holders do you consider to be the most important when building your number and why?

3. What advice would you give to a new player for maximizing their chances for building numbers closest to the target?

Remember: To make good predictions it helps to consider previous rounds of play and the combinations that happened.

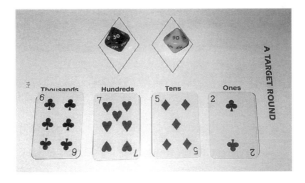

√ RADICAL RULES:

ROUNDING STRATEGIES AND TIPS:

Many of our games involve rounding practice. We have used the following strategies in grade 5 through 9 classrooms. We have experienced first hand just how much students needed this assistance. Teachers confirm that students require a lot of opportunity to practice!

You will find that both decadice and ten-sided (0-9) dice are perfect for rounding activities and practice.

We started by teaching the basic rules for rounding as outlined in the chart below:

To round to the nearest 10:	To round to the nearest 100:	To round to the nearest 1000:	To round to the nearest 10 000:	To round to the nearest 100 000:
If the ones digit is 5 or greater round up to the next 10. If it is less than 5 round down.	If the tens digit is 5 or greater round up to the next 100. If it is less than 5 round down.	If the hundreds digit is 5 or greater round up to the next 1000. If it is less than 5 round down.	If the thousands digit is 5 or greater round up to the next 10 000. If it is less than 5 round down.	If the ten thousands digit is 5 or greater round up to the next 100 000. If it is less than 5 round down.
1 37<u>6</u> rounds to 1 380 4 59<u>1</u> rounds to 4 590	4 8<u>7</u>8 rounds to 4 900 8 3<u>4</u>7 rounds to 8 300	5 <u>6</u>81 rounds to 6 000 7 <u>3</u>95 rounds to 7 000	1<u>8</u> 274 rounds to 20 000 6<u>2</u> 499 rounds to 60 000	1<u>4</u>2 391 rounds to 100 000 3<u>6</u>7 890 rounds to 400 000

We realized we had to add to this chart by teaching 'directly':

If the number you are rounding ends in 0, 1, 2, 3 or 4, that's a "stay-put" number. The place value position you are rounding "stays-put" (you'll see what we mean in our example).

If the number you are rounding ends in a 5, 6, 7, 8 or 9, that is a "round up" number. The place value position you are rounding BUMPS UP by one.

We practice these basic rules with the ten-sided (0-9) die. It is perfect for practicing basic rounding rules as it is numbered 0 through 9 and has all rounding possibilities on it.

Have students warm up for any of the rounding games by rolling the die, identifying the number and stating whether it is a "round up" or "stay put" number.

As we observed students play the rounding games we noticed that part of the difficulty they experienced when rounding numbers was identifying what place value holder to look at for rounding to the nearest 10, 100, 1 000, etc.

We found two things that really helped:

1) labeling or marking the place value position prior to rounding.

2) providing a number line of rounded numbers for a visual reference.

IN TROUBLE DOUBLES

LEVEL: Grade 6 - 9

SKILLS: Adding doubles, subtraction with regrouping

PLAYERS: 2 of equal skill level

EQUIPMENT: Two thirty-sided (1-30) dice, bingo chips or other counters

GETTING STARTED: One die is rolled between both players. Players determine the top number and double its value to determine the sum. The second die is rolled and the smaller number is subtracted from the larger.

EXAMPLE I: first die: 22 is rolled; doubled to 44
                    second die: 6 is rolled; difference is 44 - 6 = 38

EXAMPLE II: first die: 4 is rolled; doubled to 8
                    second die: 16 is rolled; difference is 16 - 8 = 8

The first player to verbalize the correct answer earns 1 point (bingo chip). In the event of a tie (i.e. both players verbalize the answer at the same time), no player earns a point. Play continues for a set period of time. The player with the most points wins.

VARIATION: **Play Triple It!**

One die is rolled between both players and the top number is tripled. The second die is rolled and the "less than" number is subtracted from the "greater than" number.

EXAMPLE: First die: 18 is rolled, tripled to 54

                    Second die: 11 is rolled; difference is 43

ADDIN' SNAPPIN'

LEVEL: Grade 6 - 9

SKILLS: Addition of two addends with regrouping

PLAYERS: 2 of equal skill level

EQUIPMENT: One thirty-sided (1-30) die per player, bingo chips or other counters

GETTING STARTED: To begin, each player rolls their die at the same time. The first player to correctly add these numbers together and say their sum out loud earns a point (bingo chip). In the event of a tie (i.e. both players give the answer at the same time) each player earns a point. Play continues for a set period of time. The player with the most points is the winner.

VARIATION I: **PLUS 10:**

Before saying the sum out loud players must add 10 (e.g. roll 14 + 21 = 35: players must say "45"). To extend this mental math activity try adding plus 5, plus 9 or plus 2, etc.

VARIATION II: **TIMES 10:**

Before verbalizing the sum players must multiply by 10 (or 100) and say the product out loud (e.g. roll 14 + 21 = 35: players must say "350 or 3 500").

OTHER VARIATIONS: Multiplication, subtraction or try mental math variations.

EXAMPLE:
1) Roll and add; mentally plus 100.
2) Roll and add; double it.
3) Roll and subtract; minus 1.

SNAPPY INTEGERS

LEVEL: Grade 7 - 9

SKILLS: Adding positive and negative integers

PLAYERS: 2 of equal skill level

EQUIPMENT: One different coloured thirty-sided (1-30) die per player, bingo chips or other counters, paper, pencil

GETTING STARTED: Players determine which coloured die equals positive values and which die equals negative values. Players roll their dice at the same time. The first player to correctly add them together and verbalize the sum earns 1 point (bingo chip or other suitable counter). In the event of a tie (i.e. both players verbalize their answer at the same time) no player earns a point. Play continues for a set period of time. The player with the most points wins.

EXAMPLE:

Player One	Player Two
(+) Positive Die	(-) Negative Die
+16	-3

The correct answer is 13

Player One	Player Two
+8	-22

The correct answer is -14.

Players may use paper and pencil to calculate answers if necessary.

VARIATION: To increase the level of difficulty, play in a group of three. Each player rolls their own thirty-sided (1-30) die and the first player to correctly add them earns the point. Players need to assign positive and negative values to the colours of the dice being rolled (e.g. 2 yellows - negative and 1 green - positive).

Player One	Player Two	Player Three
+10	-5	-17

The correct answer = -12

INTEGER ADDITION WAR

LEVEL: Grade 7 - 9

SKILLS: Adding positive and negative integers

PLAYERS: 2

EQUIPMENT: Cards Ace - King (Ace = 1, Jack = 11, Queen = 12, King = 0); assign black cards as positive and red cards as negative

GETTING STARTED: Players divide the cards evenly between themselves. Players turn over two cards each and add them.

EXAMPLE:

Player One	Player Two
red 5 + red 2 = -7	black 3 + red 4 = -1

The player with the greatest sum earns all of the cards. Player Two would verbalize "negative one is greater than negative seven." Play continues until one player has collected all of the cards.

In the event of a tie (i.e. both have the same sum), each player deals out three cards face down. Two more cards are turned face up and added. The player with the greatest sum collects all of the cards.

Player One

$$5 + 2 = 7$$ (black + black)

Player Two

$$6 + 1 = 7$$ (black + black)

WAR

Player One

$$3 + 2 = -5$$ (red + red)

Player Two

$$1 + 0 = 1$$ (black + black king)

Player Two takes all the cards.

VARIATION: Play 3 addend addition with cards still holding positive and negative values.

EXAMPLE:

Player One:	red 6 + black 2 + black 9 = 5	-6 + 2 + 9 = 5
Player Two:	black 3 + red 7 + black 1 = -3	3 + -7 + 1 = -3

Player One would collect all of the cards.

TO SUM IT UP /
WHAT'S THE DIFFERENCE?

LEVEL: Grade 6 - 9

SKILLS: Addition/subtraction with regrouping of multi-digit numbers

Variation: multiplication, division

PLAYERS: 2 - 4 or teacher vs. whole class

EQUIPMENT: One ten-sided (0-9) die, gameboard (see reproducibles), paper, pencil

GETTING STARTED: Play begins by selecting the operation that will be used for the game. The goal of the game is to:

1. Add: create the greatest sum possible.

2. Subtract: create the least difference possible.

3. Multiply: create the greatest product possible.

4. Divide: create the least quotient possible.

Players would select from any of the gameboards provided (see reproducibles).

NOTE: Gameboards can be changed to suit the levels of students within the classroom BUT all players within the group must be playing with the same gameboard once play begins. Also, players may just copy the gameboard into their math book.

One player is selected to be the roller for the round. Each player creates their gameboard. Play begins by the roller rolling the die. All players in the group must write this number down on a space on their gameboard, keeping in mind the goal for the operation selected. Numbers cannot be erased once placed.

Play continues by rolling out the rest of the numbers necessary to complete the round. When all spaces are filled in, players complete their operations and compare their gameboards to determine the winner(s) for the round. Players earn 1 point for a winning round.

A new round begins by selecting a new roller. Play continues for a set period of time. The player with the most points is the winner.

INTEGER ADDITION SNAP

LEVEL: Grade 7 - 9

SKILLS: Adding positive and negative integers

PLAYERS: 2 or more of equal skill level

EQUIPMENT: Cards Ace - King (Ace = 1, Jack = 11, Queen = 12, King = 0); assign black cards as positive and red cards as negative

GETTING STARTED: Players divide the cards evenly between themselves. Each player then turns over one card at the same time. Players must add the two numbers. The first player who says the correct sum out loud collects both cards. Play continues until one player has collected all of the cards.

In the event of a tie, both players leave their cards face down and let the pile build. Play continues until one player gives a correct answer before the other and collects all of the accumulated cards.

EXAMPLE:

Player One	**Player Two**
red 8	black 3

$$-8 + 3 = -5$$

VARIATION I: **Mental Math Activities:**

- Add the two numbers, plus 10 and answer out loud.
  e.g. $6 + -1 = 5 + 10 = 15$

- Add the two numbers and plus 1
  e.g. $-4 + 6 = 2 + 1 = 3$

- Add the two numbers and double it
  e.g. $-2 + 8 = 6 + 6 = 12$

- Add the two numbers and subtract 1, etc.
  e.g. $-11 + 5 = -6 - 1 = -7$

VARIATION II: Three players divide the cards evenly and each player turns one card over at the same time. Players must add the three numbers and call the answer out loud.

Player One	**Player Two**	**Player Three**
+12	-7	+2

Player Three is the first to verbalize "7" and earns all of the cards.

INTEGER SUBTRACTION WAR

LEVEL:	Grade 7 - 9
SKILLS:	Subtracting positive and negative integers
PLAYERS:	2
EQUIPMENT:	Cards Ace - Queen (Ace = 1, Jack = 11, Queen = 12); assign red cards as negative and black cards as positive
GETTING STARTED:	Players divide the cards evenly between themselves. Players turn over two cards each and subtract them.
EXAMPLE:	

Player One	Player Two
red 3, black 6	red 4, black 2
-3 – 6 = -9	-4 – 2 = -6

The player with the least difference collects all of the cards. Player One collects all of the cards. Play continues until one player has all of the cards.

In the event of a tie (i.e. the same difference), each player deals out three more cards face down. Two more cards are turned over and subtracted. The player with the smallest difference collects all of the cards.

Player One   **Player Two**

black		black			black		black	
5	–	**2**	= 3		**6**	–	**3**	= 3

                    WAR

red		red			black	12		
3	–	**2**	= -1		**1**	–	black queen	= -11

Player Two takes all the cards.

GET BACK TO ZERO!

LEVEL: Grade 7 - 10

SKILL: Adding and subtracting with positive and negative numbers, plotting integers on a number line, problem solving

PLAYERS: 2 - 4

EQUIPMENT: Two decadice of different colours (players designate one coloured decadie to equal negative values and the other colour to equal only positive values), one regular die, one bingo chip per player, gameboard (see reproducibles).

GETTING STARTED: The goal of the game is to be the first player to get back to zero after each player has taken a minimum of five rolls. This is a two step game.

STEP ONE:

To begin, one player rolls the regular die. This determines whether the player will add or subtract on their number line. If a player rolls an odd number (i.e. 1, 3 or 5), this indicates subtraction and an even roll of 2, 4 or 6 indicates addition.

Once the operation is determined go to Step Two.

STEP TWO:

The player must now decide which decadie to roll. The one colour that has been set aside as the negative value or the one set aside as the positive die (e.g. yellow = negative and blue = positive throughout the entire game). Players will move their bingo chip to the corresponding numbers on the line until they get back to zero.

EXAMPLE: **Player One's Moves Only**

1. Rolls 6 (must add),   chooses blue decadie (+),   rolls 10➤ 0 + 10 = 10
2. Rolls 6 (must add),   chooses yellow decadie (–), rolls 20➤ 10 + -20 = -10
3. Rolls 2 (must add),   chooses blue decadie (+),   rolls 70➤ -10 + 70 = 60
4. Rolls 3 (must subtract), chooses blue decadie (+),   rolls 80➤ 60 – 80 = -20
5. Rolls 5 (must subtract), chooses yellow decadie (–), rolls 70➤ -20 – -70 = 50
6. Rolls 1 (must subtract), chooses blue decadie (+),   rolls 20➤ 50 – 20 = 30
7. Rolls 4 (must add),   chooses yellow decadie (–), rolls 50➤ 30 + -50 = -20
8. Rolls 4 (must add),   chooses blue decadie (+),   rolls 10➤ -20 + 10 = -10
9. Rolls 2 (must add),   chooses blue decadie (+),   rolls 40➤ -10 + 40 = 30
10. Rolls 5 (must subtract), chooses blue decadie (+),   rolls 90➤ 30 – 90 = -60
11. Rolls 6 (must add),   chooses blue decadie (+),   rolls 30➤ -60 + 30 = -30
12. Rolls 4 (must add),   chooses blue decadie (+),   rolls 30➤ -30 + 30 = **0!!**

Play now ends as Player One has made it back to zero. Player One wins this round.

√ **RADICAL RULES:**

1. When you subtract a negative number, move to the right. Subtracting a negative number is the same as adding its opposite (e.g. -2 – -5 = 3).

2. When you subtract a positive number, move to the left (e.g. 4 – 8 = -4).

3. To add a negative number plus a positive, subtract the smaller absolute value from the greater. The sum has the sign of the number with the greater absolute value (e.g. 58 + -74 = -16).

4. To add a negative number plus a negative number, add their absolute values and the sum is negative (e.g. -83 + -5 = -88).

MULTIPLICATION SNAP

LEVEL: Grade 7 - 9

SKILLS: Immediate recall of multiplication facts

PLAYERS: 3 of equal skill level

EQUIPMENT: Cards Ace - King (Ace = 1, Jack = 11, Queen = 12, King = 0)

GETTING STARTED: Players divide the cards evenly into three piles. Each player has their own pile of cards. At the same time, each player turns over a card. Players multiply the three cards. The first player who verbalizes the correct product out loud collects all of the cards.

In the event of a tie, players leave their cards face down and let the pile build. Play resumes until one player gives the correct answer before the others and this player now collects all of the accumulated cards.

Play continues until the common piles are finished. Players count up their cards to determine the winner.

VARIATION: At the same time, players roll one multi-sided die each (i.e. one ten-sided (0-9) die, one twelve-sided (1-12) die and one thirty-sided (1-30) die). The first player to multiply all three numbers and correctly verbalize their product wins.

TEACHING TIP: An additional player may join the group to become the "judge". This player checks for accuracy of the answers by using a calculator.

THREE FOR ME

LEVEL: Grade 6 - 9

SKILLS: Multiplying to 144

PLAYERS: 2

EQUIPMENT: Two twelve-sided (1-12) dice, gameboard (see reproducibles), bingo chips - two colours (or other markers)

GETTING STARTED: Players use one gameboard. Each player chooses a colour of bingo chips. Player One rolls the dice, multiplies them, and places their chips on possible combinations of that product.

EXAMPLE: Player One rolls 6 and 4, and places chips on combinations for 24, (i.e. 6 x 4 and 4 x 6 and 3 x 8 and 8 x 3 and 12 x 2 and 2 x 12).

	1	2	3	4	5	6	7	8	9	10	11	12
1	1	2	3	4	5	6	7	8	9	10	11	12
2	2	4	6	8	10	12	14	16	18	20	22	24
3	3	6	9	12	15	18	21	24	27	30	33	36
4	4	8	12	16	20	24	28	32	36	40	44	48
5	5	10	15	20	25	30	35	40	45	50	55	60
6	6	12	18	24	30	36	42	48	54	60	66	72
7	7	14	21	28	35	42	49	56	63	70	77	84
8	8	16	24	32	40	48	56	64	72	80	88	96
9	9	18	27	36	45	54	63	72	81	90	99	108
10	10	20	30	40	50	60	70	80	90	100	110	120
11	11	22	33	44	55	66	77	88	99	110	121	132
12	12	24	36	48	60	72	84	96	108	120	132	144

Player One verbalizes that their turn is now over. Player Two may then cover any missed combinations by Player One, with their own bingo chips. Since Player One did cover up all possible combinations, this was not possible for Player Two. Player Two then rolls 7 and 12 and puts chips on combinations for 84 (i.e. 7 x 12 and 12 x 7).

Players alternate rolling the dice and placing chips on the board. The goal is for players to get three chips in a row either horizontally, vertically, or diagonally. If a player gets three in a row, they take them off the board and they become "keepers". They will be used at the end of the game as points to calculate the player's final score. If a player rolls their own number they may re-roll or "crown" this number.

Capturing a Player's Chip: If a player rolls a number that is already occupied by their opponent, they can capture it. They take their opponent's chip and replace it with their own. The captured chip is kept by the roller, and becomes a "keeper". It will be used at the end of the game to determine their final score.

Determining the Winner: After a set period of time the game ends. To determine the score, keepers are counted as follows:

Keepers of the player's own colour = 2 points each
Keepers of the opponent's colour = 5 points each
Own chips left on the board = 1 point each

The player with the most points wins.

TEACHING TIP:

To increase the level of difficulty, players use a blank multiplication board and fill in the answers using coloured markers of different colours. When a player gets three answers of their own colour on the board they draw a ring around these numbers and score 1 point. Players do not capture each others spaces in this variation.

MULTIPLICATION SCRAMBLE

LEVEL: Grade 6 - 9

SKILLS: Multiplication facts to 144, probability

PLAYERS: 1 to 2

EQUIPMENT: Two twelve-sided (1-12) dice or cards Ace - King (Ace = 1, Jack = 11, Queen = 12, King = 0), gameboard (see reproducibles)

GETTING STARTED: The goal of this game is to fill in every line on the scramble grid. Each player rolls two dice and multiplies the numbers. Players write down their product in the appropriate space on their gameboard (e.g. 4 x 9 = 36, so 36 would go in the space for 30 - 39). If a player rolls a product and that space has already been filled in, that player now misses their turn (i.e. no space is filled in for that roll). Play continues until one player successfully fills in all of the spaces on their gameboard.

EXAMPLE:

	Player One	Player Two
0 - 9		
10 - 19		6 X 2 = 12
20 - 29	① 7 X 4 = 28	5 X 5 = 25
30 - 39	4 X 8 = 32	② 5 X 6 = 30
40 - 49	③ 9 X 5 = 45	
50 - 59		
60 - 69		⑥ 10 X 5 = 50
70 - 79	9 X 8 = 72	
80 - 89	11 X 8 = 88	
90 - 99		
100 - 109	⑤ 10 X 10 = 100	
110 - 119		
120 - 129		
130 - 139		
140 - 149		

Player One ① rolls or turns over 7 X 4 = 28

Player Two ② rolls or turns over 5 X 6 = 30

Player One ③ rolls or turns over 9 X 5 = 45

Player Two ④ rolls or turns over 5 X 6 = 30 does not fill in anything

Player One ⑤ rolls or turns over 10 x 10 = 100

Player Two ⑥ rolls or turns over 10 X 5 = 50

VARIATION I: To decrease the level of difficulty, use cards from Ace - 9 (Ace = 1) and use grid only up to 80 - 89.

0 -	9	_____
10 -	19	_____
20 -	29	_____
30 -	39	_____
40 -	49	_____
50 -	59	_____
60 -	69	_____
70 -	79	_____
80 -	89	_____

VARIATION II: Add rounding to the skill level of the game by using the following gameboard:

0	_____
10	_____
20	_____
30	_____
40	_____
50	_____
60	_____
70	_____
80	_____
90	8 x 11 = 88
100	_____
110	_____
120	_____
130	_____
140	_____

Players roll two twelve-sided (1-12) dice, multiply them and round their product off to the nearest ten. The player now records this in the appropriate space. The first player to fill in their gameboard wins.

EXAMPLE: 8 x 11 = 88, rounds to 90

THOUGHT PROVOKERS:

Have students figure out the average number of rolls to fill in all spaces on the scramble grid.

PRODUCTIVE PONDERING

LEVEL: Grade 6 - 9

SKILLS: Multiplying two-digit numbers, estimation, mental math

PLAYERS: 2 to 4

EQUIPMENT: Two thirty-sided (1-30) dice, paper, pencil

GETTING STARTED: The goal of the game is to be the player with the closest prediction to the sum of all the products. Each player rolls two dice five times and records all five multiplication sentences. Before starting their calculation each player must predict what their combined sum of their five products will be. The player who is closest to their prediction is the winner.

EXAMPLE: Player predicts: 1 125

Roll One:	$27 \times 6 =$	162
Roll Two:	$11 \times 22 =$	242
Roll Three:	$2 \times 16 =$	32
Roll Four:	$13 \times 15 =$	195
Roll Five:	$20 \times 25 =$	<u>500</u>
ACTUAL TOTAL SUM:		1 131

Prediction 1 125, actual sum = 1 131

Difference of 6.

After all players have calculated their products and totalled their sums, they now compare the accuracy of their predictions. The player closest to their prediction (i.e. least difference) wins the round.

VARIATIONS: Vary the number of rolls allowed. Calculate class averages of total combined sum and difference from predictions.

FOOTBALL FACTOR

LEVEL: Grade 6 - 9

SKILLS: Multiplying 10's and 1's, multiple addend addition, probability

PLAYERS: 2

EQUIPMENT: One decadie, gameboard (see reproducibles), pencil

GETTING STARTED: The goal of the game is to have the greatest number of points after four quarters. Players start off by choosing a "touch down factor". This value will be multiplied by the dice roll to determine the points earned for a touch down.

TEACHING TIP: Encourage students to select the times tables that they need to practice the most (e.g. 6 x, 7 x, 8 x, 12 x).

Player One starts by rolling the decadie and multiplying the die by the touch down factor to determine their touch down score. Player One then rolls a second decadie. This value is the field goal score. It is added to the touch down score to determine the total score for the first quarter.

The next player takes their turn and play continues until both players have played four quarters.

Players can record their scores in the Football Factor gameboard (see reproducibles).

EXAMPLE: Teams choose 6 to be the touch down factor.

Player One, First Quarter

Touch Down Roll:

Touch Down Score = 6 x 90 = 540

Field Goal Roll:

Field Goal Score = 40

Player One's total score for the first quarter is 580 (540 + 40).

Player Two, First Quarter

Touch Down Roll:

Touch Down Score = 6 x 80 = 480

Field Goal Roll:

Field Goal Score = 90

Player Two's total score for the first quarter is 570 (480 + 90).

Player One

	Touchdown	Field Goal	Total
1st Quarter	6 x 90 = 540	40	540 + 40 = 580
2nd Quarter	6 x 40 = 240	30	240 + 30 = 270
3rd Quarter	6 x 20 = 120	90	120 + 90 = 210
4th Quarter	6 x 70 = 420	00	420 + 00 = 420

Total Football Score 1480

Player Two

	Touchdown	Field Goal	Total
1st Quarter	6 x 80 = 480	90	480 + 90 = 570

Play continues until all four quarters are played out. The player with the greatest accumulated point total is the winner.

Encourage players to change the touch down factor so that they can practice all the times tables - especially 6 x, 7 x, 8 x and 12 x.

THOUGHT PROVOKERS:

Have all the students play the same scoring system and record all totals.

1. What is the average point total when the touch down factor is 6? Once this is determined, predict and test out how this average will change when the touch down factor is 7 or 8, etc.

The following samples show 56 games played out in a class. Scores were arranged to determine median.

NOTE: The median was the same as the average. AMAZING!!

Foot ball Factor   7-3

90, 160, 310, 1080, 1120, 1300, 1340, 1400, 1420,

1440, 1460, 1460, 1470, 1470, 1550, 1550, 1630,

1640, 1640, 1690, 1700, 1730, 1760, 1850,

1890, 1890, 1900, $\boxed{1930}$, 1940, 1950, 1960,

1960, 1990, 2100, 2150, 2160, 2160, 2170,

2190, 2200, 2340, 2350, 2380, 2430,

2480, 2480, 2600, 2670, 2700, 2750,

2840, 2860, 2890, 2990, 3190, 3300?

NOTE: Class scores arranged in order to determine median. The class was amazed to see how closely it matched the mean (average).

56 games
Range 90 - 3300
Average - 1929·46
28 game 1930·

Total 108 050

max score per quarter (90×8) +90 = 810
per game 810×4 = 3240.

I think football factor is a really kool game because it was really easy to play and it was neat that we got our average on the 28th game.

Melissa Sutherland

I think football faction is a great game for loosening your multiplication and addition skills. I thought that it was interesting that we got our average by the 28 game that we played.

Felisha Corbeil
7-3
Nov 15,00

Zach Kipp 7-3

Football on factor was fun because I knew multiplycation and it was very easy for me. The night, last night I played with my brother and said it was fun because he knew multiply and it was good practice for him.

Garret Hannah 7-3

Football factors was fun because my favorite sport is football and its fun to play games instead of do work

Loved football factors.
You always have something todo. You can do you're partners in you're head. It helped me with my math alot.

Mikayla Kessler
7-3
Nov. 15/00
Paula V.

Football Factor

I though Football Factor was a fun game because I like to multiply and it pushed me to work fast and memorize the 8's.

Football Factor 8-2

160, 300, 520, 640, 1020, 1110, 1170, 1330, 1360, 1370, 1440, 1460, 1480, 1510, 1540, 1600, 1610, 1670, 1740, 1810.

1900, 1910, 1930, [1930], 2010, 2030, 2050, 2060

2060, 2060, 2070, 2130, 2160, 2170, 2210, 2220, 2280

2310, 2470, 2480, 2500, 2530, 2530, 2540, 2580

2640, 2650, 2960, 2980

50 games
Range 160-2980
Average - 1825.80
Total score 91290
25th game - 1930.

51

RED RACERS CHALLENGER

LEVEL: Grade 6 - 9

SKILLS: Multiplying by multiples of 10's, probability

PLAYERS: 2

EQUIPMENT: Two decadice per player, one gameboard per player (see reproducibles), pencil

GETTING STARTED: **STEP ONE - Qualifying Laps:**

Players roll both dice, multiplying the two numbers, and writing the product on their chart under the Q (for Qualifying Lap). Once both players have completed the rolls on their own charts, the gameboards are exchanged and Elimination begins.

STEP TWO - Elimination Laps:

Players alternate rolling both dice ten times each, this time attempting to eliminate their opponent's products. If a player rolls a product that occurs more than once, both of these numbers would be eliminated at the same time. In the example below, Player Two has two 800's and both would be eliminated if Player One rolls 20 x 40 or 10 x 80.

EXAMPLE: After ten rolls, players' boards look like this:

Player One	Q		Player Two	Q
10×80	$= 800$		60×40	$= 2400$
50×20	$= 1000$		10×80	$= 800$
70×60	$= 4200$		60×60	$= 3600$
00×00	$= 0$		40×20	$= 800$
20×90	$= 1800$		40×40	$= 1600$
00×90	$= 0$		40×40	$= 1600$
40×40	$= 1600$		90×40	$= 3600$
70×80	$= 5600$		20×30	$= 400$
20×80	$= 1600$		50×20	$= 1000$
10×30	$= 300$		60×70	$= 4200$

Once the Q round has been completed individually by both players, the gameboards are exchanged. Both players now roll out ten new products. If they roll any product that appears on their opponent's gameboard they may cross it off.

The player who eliminates the most products wins.

Player One Q	E Player Two's Elimination Rolls
~~10 x 80 = 800~~	00 x 60 = 0 - eliminates two products
50 x 20 = 1000	60 x 90 = 540
70 x 60 = 4200	30 x 70 = 210
~~00 x 00 = 0~~	10 x 80 = 800 - eliminates one
20 x 90 = 1800	00 x 90 = 0
~~00 x 90 = 0~~	40 x 50 = 200
~~40 x 40 = 1600~~	70 x 40 = 280
70 x 80 = 5600	40 x 40 = 1600 - eliminates two
~~20 x 80 = 1600~~	00 x 60 = 0
10 x 30 = 300	10 x 40 = 400

Player Two eliminates a total of 5. Players return gameboards to their opponents. The player who has eliminated the greatest number of products is the winner.

A new round begins by players rolling ten new products in Qualifying (Step One).

THOUGHT PROVOKERS:

1. Which numbers are easiest to eliminate?

2. Develop the outcome chart for all possible products that can be rolled. Develop a system for organizing your answer.

3. Calculate the average number of "eliminations" per round.

ROLL OF THE MILLENNIUM

LEVEL: Grade 6 - 9

SKILLS: Multiplying tens, hundreds, rounding, multiple addend addition, subtraction, probability

PLAYERS: 2

EQUIPMENT: Two decadice, paper, pencil

GETTING STARTED: Players alternate rolling both dice and multiplying the two numbers together. The player with the product closest to any millennium (1 000's number) earns the points for that round.

Player One	Player Two
60 x 40 = 2 400	80 x 90 = 7 200

Player Two earns 200 points as 7 200 is closer to 7 000 than 2 400 is to 2 000. The points a player earns is determined by the "millennium difference" from the closest thousand number. For example, 3 400 would earn a player 400 points if that player's number was closest; 1 700 would earn 300 points for closest to 2 000, etc. Players must always consider both adding and subtracting to the nearest thousand number. If numbers are equally close to the nearest thousand, players tie and no one earns points. If a player gets a multiple of 1 000 (or 0) they automatically earn 1 000 points.

Players keep a running tally of their own points. The first player to reach 5 000 points is the winner.

THOUGHT PROVOKERS:

1. On average, how many rolls do you think it will take one player to reach 5 000?

2. If the rules were written so the player with the product furthest from any thousand number earns the points, would the game end quicker? Why or why not?

MULTIPLICATION MATCH UP

LEVEL: Grade 6 - 9

SKILLS: Multiplying two-digit numbers

PLAYERS: 2

EQUIPMENT: Two thirty-sided (1-30) dice per player, bingo chips or other counters, calculators (optional), paper, pencil

GETTING STARTED: Each player rolls their two dice and multiplies these two numbers. The player with the greatest product earns a point (bingo chip).

EXAMPLE:

Player One	**Player Two**
$3 \times 14 = 42$	$11 \times 30 = 330$

Player Two earns a point. It is obvious with the above example which player would have the greatest product. It is IMPORTANT that both players verbalize their math sentence before a player earns a point.

In the event of a tie (i.e. both players have the same product) a tie breaker must be played. Each player rolls their dice again and calculates the new product. The player with the greatest product earns a point.

EXAMPLE:

Player One	**Player Two**
$4 \times 12 = 48$	$6 \times 8 = 48$

Tie "48"

TIE BREAKER

$16 \times 10 = 160$	$14 \times 7 = 98$

Player One earns a point. Play continues for a set period of time. The player with the most points is the winner.

Paper and pencil may be used and calculators may be used to check for accuracy.

INTEGER MULTIPLICATION WAR

LEVEL: Grade 7 - 9

SKILLS: Multiplying positive and negative integers

PLAYERS: 2 or more

EQUIPMENT: Cards Ace - King (Ace = 1, Jack = 11, Queen = 12, King = 0); assign black cards as positive and red cards as negative

GETTING STARTED: Players divide cards evenly between themselves. Players turn over two cards each and multiply them. The player with the highest product collects all four cards. Play continues until one player has all of the cards.

In the event of a tie (i.e. the same answer), each player deals three more cards face down. Two more cards are turned over and multiplied. The player with the highest product collects all of the cards.

EXAMPLE:

Player One	Player Two
red 7, red 5	red 3, black 6
= -7 x -5 = 35	= -3 x 6 = -18

Player One collects all four cards.

VARIATION: To increase the level of difficulty, have players turn over three cards each and multiply to find the product. The player with the highest product earns all of the cards.

EXAMPLE:

Player One	Player Two
black 2, red 4, red 7	black 1, black 6, red 3
2(-4)(-7) = 56	1(6)(-3) = -18

INTEGER MULTIPLICATION SNAP

LEVEL: Grade 7 - 10

SKILLS: Multiplying positive and negative integers

PLAYERS: 2 or more of equal skill level

EQUIPMENT   Cards Ace - King (Ace = 1, Jack = 11, Queen = 12, King = 0); assign black cards as positive and red cards as negative

GETTING STARTED: Players divide the cards evenly between themselves. At the same time, each player turns over one card. Players must multiply the two numbers. The first player to verbalize the correct product out loud collects both cards. Play continues until one player has collected all of the cards.

In the event of a tie, players leave their cards face down and let the pile build. Play continues until one player gives a correct answer before the other and takes all of the accumulated cards.

EXAMPLE:

Player One	Player Two	
black 4	black 6	4 x 6 = 24
red 7	black 3	-7 x 3 = -21

VARIATION: To increase the level of difficulty, have three players of equal skill level play. Players now multiply three numbers.

EXAMPLE:

Player One	Player Two	Player Three
Red 9	Red 4	Black 2

The first player to verbalize "seventy-two" earns all of the cards.

KNOCKING INTEGERS

LEVEL: Grade 8 - 10

SKILLS: Multiplication with integers

PLAYERS: 4 or 5

EQUIPMENT: Cards Ace - King (Ace = 1, Jack = 11, Queen = 12, King = 0), paper, pencil

GETTING STARTED: Each player is dealt three cards. Two piles are left in the center of the players. One pile is face down and one pile is face up (the discard pile). The player to the right of the dealer begins. The object of the game is to create either the greatest or the least product using your three cards. Red cards are negative and black cards are positive. During their turn players may select one card from either pile and choose to keep it, discarding a card from their hand or discarding the card chosen. Play continues until one player decides to keep their hand and knocks to indicate that the other players have only one more turn to build the best possible hand. The player with the greatest earns 1 point. The player with the least earns 1 point. Players show their hands to determine the winners.

VARIATION: Players declare whether they have the greatest or least product (before comparing) and only receive a point if their prediction was correct.

EXAMPLE:

PLAYER ONE	PLAYER TWO	PLAYER THREE
+6 +11 -3	-2 -7 -4	5 -7 -12
= -198	= -56	= 420

Both Player Two and Player Three earn 1 point in the above round of play.

ALL THAT REMAINS

LEVEL: Grade 6 - 9

SKILLS: Dividing

PLAYERS: 2

EQUIPMENT: Three thirty-sided (1-30) dice, calculator, paper, pencil

GETTING STARTED: Each player begins the game with a score of 30.

Player One rolls two dice and creates a number in place value (i.e. a two, three or four-digit number). This number becomes the dividend in the number equation. Player One rolls one die as the divisor. Player One divides the numbers and calculates the remainder. The remainder is subtracted from the beginning score of 30.

Players alternate turns until one player reaches a score of 0.

EXAMPLE:

Player One

Rolls two dice: 11, 5 = 115 or 511
Player chooses 115
Rolls one die = 8 $115 \div 8 = 14$ R. 3
3 is the remainder
TO SCORE: 30 - 3 = 27

Player Two

Roll two dice: 2, 17 = 217 or 172
Player chooses 217
Rolls one die = 28 $217 \div 28 = 7$ R. 21
TO SCORE: 30 - 21 = 9

Play to zero or if a player exceeds 0 they also win.

DIVISION DECISION

LEVEL: Grade 6 - 9

SKILLS: Division with remainders

PLAYERS: 2

EQUIPMENT: Three thirty-sided (1-30) dice, paper, pencil, hundred board (see reproducibles), bingo chips or other markers

GETTING STARTED: The goal of the game is to be the first player to reach 100 on the hundred board. Players both begin by placing their marker on number 1. Player One begins by rolling the three thirty-sided (1-30) dice and arranges them into a division equation. The player now divides the numbers as set and figures out the remainder. Players move their marker along the hundred board equal to the remainder of the equation. Players must analyze and set their numbers to maximize the greatest possible remainder.

EXAMPLE: Player One rolls: 17, 5, 26

Possible Configurations:

$5 \overline{)1726}$ = 345.2 = 345 R.1

Player One moves ahead on the hundred board the number of spaces equal to the remainder. In this example, Player One chooses:

$$26 \overline{)517}$$

$17 \overline{)526}$ = 30.94 = 30 R.16

$26 \overline{)175}$ = 6.73 = 6 R.19

$5 \overline{)2617}$ = 523.4 = 523 R.2

$17 \overline{)265}$ = 15.58 = 15 R.10

$26 \overline{)517}$ = 19.88 = 19 R.23

Player One moves ahead 19 spaces to number 20. Player Two now takes their turn rolling the dice, dividing the numbers and finding the remainder.

If a player divides the numbers and there is no remainder then that player does not move forward on their board. Players continue to alternate turns and move along the hundred board. The first player to reach 100 wins.

MATH FOOTBALL

(submitted by Nancy McGuire)

LEVEL: Grade 7 - 10

SKILLS: Multiplication of integers, multiplication, addition of integers, algebra

PLAYERS: 6 of equal ability (2 vs. 2 and 2 referees - team)

EQUIPMENT: One marker (football), gameboards (see reproducibles), bingo chips for markers (used for downs), one thirty-sided (1-30) die, one ten-sided (0-9) die, one twelve-sided (1-12) die

GETTING STARTED: Players move up and down the playing field in order to score points in a set amount of time. Each of the following variations follow the rules of the basic game. The differences are the mathematical concept being practiced and the particular dice used.

BASIC GAME: Each team lines up on one side of the field. The referees are in the middle. Using two twelve-sided (1-12) dice, each team rolls the dice and multiplies to decide who is the Home team. Greatest product is the Home Team and goes first. The marker (ball) is placed on the Home team's 20 yard line. The Home team has 4 downs in which to score a goal. The referee puts a bingo chip in the first down square to show that it is first down. The referee also puts a bingo chip in the Home's Ball square to show that the Home team has possession of the ball. Home team rolls the two dice and each team calls out the product. The refereeing team determines which team called out the product first. If the Visitor team calls out the product first, no yardage is gained and the play moves to second down. If the Home team calls out the product first, then yardage is gained for the Home team. The thirty-sided (1-30) die is now rolled to determine the amount of yardage gained for the Home team. If, for example, a 17 is rolled, then a player on the Home team moves the ball 17 yards toward their goal line (20 + 17 = 37 - moving towards the visitor's touchdown line).

After the result (i.e. progress stopped, or yardage gained) for the first down has been completed, then the referee places another bingo chip in the second down square to signify that it is second down. Play repeats for the second, third and fourth downs, or until a touchdown is made (0 line). If, after the fourth down the Home team (the team with possession of the ball) has not reached a touchdown, the ball turns over. The opposition takes possession of the football where it lies. The Visitor team now takes possession of the ball. The referee moves the possession bingo chip over to the Visitor side, removes the down markers from the previous set of downs, and puts a chip down to signify that it is the Visitor's first down. Play continues as above for 4 downs, or until a touchdown is scored, then the ball changes possession again.

Scoring: 6 points are scored for a touchdown

Extra points: The scoring team has an option to "go for" either 1 or 2 extra points. The team has to tell the opposing team which they are trying for.

To score 1 point, the team in possession of the ball rolls the dice and must call out the product before the opposing team, once.

To score 2 points, the team in possession must call out the product before the opposing team, twice.

 **TEACHING TIP:** To make teams of equal ability, give a one minute fast multiplication test. Correct it together as a class. Order the tests from greatest to least and select two at a time to make teams. The refereeing team has to be of equal ability as well. Be aware that this activity gets animated when you have several games going at once, but it is fun to see the kids so into their game that they don't even notice the other games going on at the same time.

Meet the needs of all your students by varying the games as necessary in the classroom. Your higher students could be playing any of the more difficult Variations while another group of lesser ability could be playing the Basic Game.

VARIATION I: Use a ten-sided (0-9) die and a twelve-sided (1-12) die, making one positive and one negative. Have players add, subtract, or multiply the dice then call out the solution. Choose only one operation at a time.

VARIATION II: Roll three, four, or five regular dice and have students multiply all of them.

VARIATION III: Roll a ten-sided (0-9) die and a twelve-sided (1-12) die, or two of the same dice in different colours. Designate one die as the denominator and one as the numerator and have students call out the fraction in its simplified form.

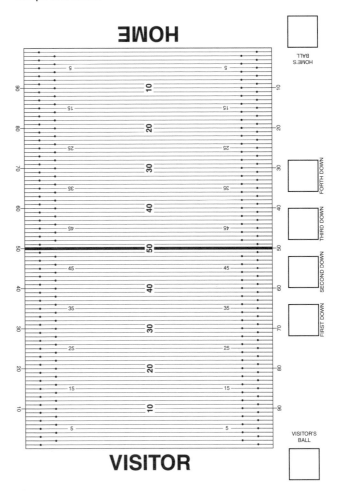

DECADE DIVISION

LEVEL: Grade 6 - 9

SKILLS: Dividing two-digit numbers into three and four-digit numbers, division with zeros, front end estimation

PLAYERS: 2

EQUIPMENT: One decadie, one thirty-sided (1-30) die, pencil, one gameboard per player (see reproducibles), scrap paper, calculator (optional)

GETTING STARTED: The goal of the game is to be the player with the closest estimated answer. To begin, Player One rolls the dice to create a division equation for both players to use as follows:

DECADE DIE		THIRTY-SIDED DIE	DECADE DIE
Divisor		Dividend	

NOTE: If a 00 is rolled, players can choose to re-roll it.

Player One rolls: $60 \overline{)2\ 280}$

Both players now record this on their gameboard and write down their estimated quotient on a separate piece of paper.

Players are not calculating the answer by "doing the actual computation"; rather they are simply making a guess using front-end estimation. Estimated answers should be recorded quickly and then verbalized out loud. Once players have shared their estimated answers, they can begin to calculate the actual answer (calculators can be used to check for accuracy only).

Players now compare their estimated answers to the actual quotient. The player with the answer closest to their estimation circles this on their gameboard to earn 1 point. If both players equal the quotient or are as equally close, they both circle their estimated answers and receive 1 point.

EXAMPLE: Player One's Gameboard Only

$50\overline{)2300}$	Estimated Answer **42**	}
	Actual Answer **46**	

Player Two's answer of 47 was closer and was circled on their gameboard (not shown).

$80\overline{)1680}$	Estimated Answer **(21)**
	Actual Answer **21**

$60\overline{)1930}$	Estimated Answer **(35)**	}
	Actual Answer **32**	

Player One was closer to Player Two's answer of 37.

$20\overline{)440}$	Estimated Answer **(22)**
	Actual Answer **22**

So far, Player One has earned 3 points.

To determine the overall winner, players count up the number of circled answers on their gameboard and the player with the most wins.

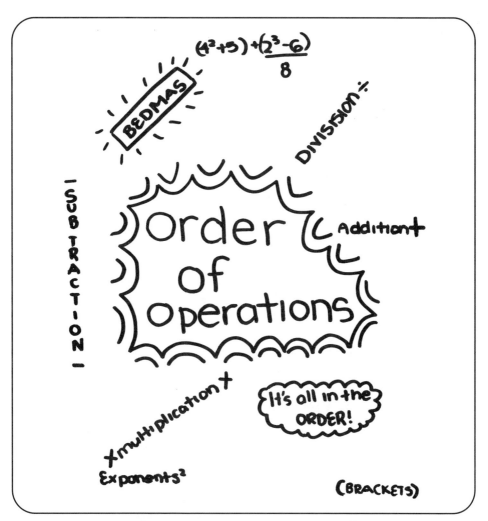

Order of Operations

OPERATIONS MIXER

LEVEL: Grade 6 - 10

SKILLS: Problem solving, order of operations

PLAYERS: Teacher vs. groups or pairs

EQUIPMENT: Cards Ace - King (Ace = 1, Jack = 11, Queen = 12, King = 0), paper, pencil

GETTING STARTED: The teacher draws two cards and makes a two-digit number (e.g. 7 and 3 make seventy-three). This number is displayed to the whole group. Each group or pair selects four cards. The players work co-operatively, manipulating the cards to arrive at the number created by the teacher. Students can multiply, add, subtract or divide, or do any combination, but each card can only be used once. When finished setting their cards, players record their math.

EXAMPLE: Teacher turns over 73. Group One draws 4, 6, 3, 1. Cards are used as follows:

$4 \times 6 \times 3 + 1 = 73$

Group Two draws 5, 10, 6, 7. Cards are used as follows:

$10 \times 6 + 7 + 5 = 72$

Only Group One would score a point for this round. Play continues for a set period of time. The group with the most points wins.

If no group is able to target the number, the group closest to (may be over target) scores the point for the round. All groups that target exactly can score.

VARIATION: If a player or group can manipulate their cards to reach the target number in two different ways, they can earn double points.

MIXED UP TIC TAC TOE

LEVEL: Grade 6 - 9

SKILLS: Problem solving, order of operations

PLAYERS: 2 to 4

EQUIPMENT: Three thirty-sided (1-30) dice, thirty bingo chips per player - own colour, hundred board (see reproducibles)

GETTING STARTED: Players roll one die each and the player with the highest number goes first. The first player chooses to roll one, two, or three dice. The numbers rolled on each die can only be used once. The player must use all numbers to come up with an answer. The player places a chip on the corresponding number. The next player then takes their turn. The first player to get three in a row horizontally, vertically or diagonally wins.

EXAMPLE: Roll 2, 18, 10

Player One calculates 2 x 18 + 10 and places their chip on 46.

NOTE: A player can "bump" another player from a square by getting the same answer as the one covered by an opponent's chip. The player puts their chip on the space after requesting their opponent to remove theirs.

1	2	3	4	5	6	7	8	9	10
11	12	13	14	15	16	17	18	19	20
21	22	23	24	25	26	27	28	29	30
31	32	33	34	35	36	37	38	39	40
41	42	43	44	45	(46)	47	48	49	50
51	52	53	54	(55)	56	57	58	59	60
61	62	63	(64)	65	66	67	68	69	70
71	72	73	74	75	76	77	78	79	80
81	82	83	84	85	86	87	88	89	90
91	92	93	94	95	96	97	98	99	100

EXAMPLE:

Player One rolls 23, 17, 15

$(17 + 15) - 23 = 9$
$23 + 17 + 15 = 55$
$(23 - 17) \times 15 = 90$
etc.
Player selects 55.

Player can use any ONE of these combinations or one of their choosing to come up with an answer.

Player Two rolls 8, 3, 11
$(8 - 3) \times 11 = 55$

Removes Player One's 55 and puts one of their own down.

Player One rolls 28, 8, 26
$(28 - 8) + 26 = 46$

Player Two rolls 6, 15, 26
$(6 \times 15) - 26 = 64$ etc.

MULTI OPERATION BLACKOUT

LEVEL: Grade 6 - 9

SKILLS: Order of operations, exponents, square roots, problem solving

PLAYERS: 2 vs. 2

EQUIPMENT: Two ten-sided (0-9) dice and one twelve-sided (1-12) die, two hundred boards, one per team (see reproducibles), bingo chips or other markers

GETTING STARTED: The goal of the game is to be the first team to cover up every number on their hundreds chart. Team One rolls the three dice. Players figure out all of the combinations they can make with the three numbers using all operations.

EXAMPLE: Roll 6, 9, 2

NOTE: Both teams work with these numbers for the three minutes.

$6 + 9 + 2 = 17$	Player may cover up
$(9 - 6) + 2 = 5$	numbers 17, 5, 56, 3,
$(9 \times 6) + 2 = 56$	1, 11, 45, 75, etc.
$(6 \times 2) - 9 = 3$	
$6^2 + 9 = 45$	
$9^2 - 6 = 75$	
$\sqrt{9} \times 2 \div 6 = 1$	
$\sqrt{9} + 2 + 6 = 11$	

etc.

For every answer calculated, teams cover the corresponding number on their hundred board. Teams are allowed a maximum of three minutes per roll. Teams alternate turns until one team successfully covers up all of their numbers.

NOTE: Players could keep a written record of their rolls and multi operation sequences.

VARIATION I: Only one team works covering up the numbers while the other team observes.

At the end of a team's time limit the opposing team can "capture" any number combinations that their opponents have missed. In the above example, Team One had missed 87 ($9^2 + 6 = 87$). Team Two can cover 87 on their gameboard as a capture).

VARIATION II: Use two twenty-sided (1-20) dice of one colour and one ten-sided (0-9) die of a different colour. Choose one set of dice as positive and the other as negative.

SWEET 16

"A REAL FAVOURITE"

LEVEL: Grade 6 and up

SKILLS: Order of operations, problem solving

PLAYERS: 1 (solitaire) or whole class in cooperative teams

EQUIPMENT: One thirty-sided (1-30) die, cards Ace - King (Ace = 1, Jack = 11, Queen = 12, King = 0)

GETTING STARTED: All teams build a 4 x 4 grid with sixteen random cards, face up.

The goal of the game is for each team to remove all the cards from their grid. All cards remaining at the end of a round equal their face value score AGAINST the team (e.g. 4 and 3 left - score against = 7). The lowest and best possible score per round is zero.

To begin, the teacher rolls a target number for the first round with the die. This number will be used by all cooperative teams. Teams now begin finding combinations that equal the target number rolled - all operations may be used. Players may take off three, four or five card combinations.

EXAMPLE: Grid was randomly drawn as follows:

King (0)	4	10	2
Jack (11)	3	9	7
6	Ace (1)	8	6
5	4	10	2

Target rolled = 9

The team made the following combinations and removed the cards as follows:

1. (Jack) 11 - 2 + 0 (King) = 9
2. (10 + 8) - 9 = 9
3. (10 - 7) + 6 = 9
4. (4 + 5) x 1 = 9
5. (3 - 2) x (4 + 5) = 9

NO CARDS REMAIN - SCORE FOR ROUND ONE = 0

After each round a new grid is drawn and a new TARGET is rolled. Teams play five rounds and accumulate their score AGAINST one another. The lowest team score after five rounds wins.

 **TEACHING TIP:** Try not to give any strategy tips - let teams discover this as they play. An important part of this game is analyzing all sixteen cards carefully before removing any simple combinations. As well, it is important to analyze the number of large card values and the low card values. Other strategies may include dividing to get a 1 or subtracting to get a 0. Have teams record all combinations and take the time to discuss strategies, difficulties and successes!

VARIATIONS: Black cards are positive and all red cards are negative. Do not allow any two card combinations.

COMBO FIVE CHALLENGER

LEVEL: Grade 7 - 10

SKILLS: Order of operations, exponents, square roots

PLAYERS: 2 vs. 2 or in groups vs. the teacher

EQUIPMENT: One thirty-sided (1-30) die, cards Ace - King (Ace = 1, Jack = 11, Queen = 12, King = 0), paper, pencil

GETTING STARTED: Player One rolls the die to determine the starting target number. Each player has five cards face up from which to play. The goal is to use as many of the five cards and any of the operations using brackets and/or exponents if necessary to equal the target number as well as the nine numbers following the target number. A team scores 1 point for each card used in a sentence and sums the 10 scores for a total score for the round. Play continues for a set amount of time. The team with the most points is the winner.

EXAMPLE:

Player One: 3 11 10 9 7

Target Number: 18

$18 = 9 + 7 + 3 - 11 + 10$	5 pts
$19 = (9 + 7 + 3) \times (11 - 10)$	5 pts
$20 = 9 + 7 + 3 + 11 - 10$	5 pts
$21 = 3 \times 11 - 10 + 7 - 9$	5 pts
$22 = 3 \times 7 + 11 - 10$	4 pts
$23 = 3 \times 10 - 7$	3 pts
$24 = 3 \times 9 - 10 + 7$	4 pts
$25 = (11 - 9)^3 + 7 + 10$	5 pts
$26 = 11 + 10 + 9 - 7 + 3$	5 pts
$27 = 11 + 9 + 7$	3 pts
	44 pts

Player Two: | 11 | 8 | 5 | 9 | 4 |

$18 = 11 - 5$
$+ 4 + 8$ — 4 pts
$19 = (11 + 8) \times [9 \div (5 + 4)]$ — 5 pts
$20 = 5 \times 4 \times (9 - 8)$ — 4 pts
$21 = (9 - 5) \times 8 - 11$ — 4 pts
$22 = [(5 - 4) + (9 - 8)] \times 11$ — 5 pts
$23 = (8 - 5) \times 4 + 11$ — 4 pts
$24 = (11 - 8) \times 5 + 9$ — 4 pts
$25 = 5^{(11-9)}$ — 3 pts
$26 = 8 + 5 + 9 + 4$ — 4 pts
$27 = 11 - 5 + 4 + 9 + 8$ — <u>5 pts</u>
— 42 pts

VARIATION I: Players may choose how many numbers after the target number they wish to use.

VARIATION II: Players use red cards as negative integers and black cards as positive integers. The target number is rolled with a thirty-sided (1-30) die. One colour of thirty-sided can be designated positive and the other negative or a player may use a regular die to determine the sign of the target number:

1, 2, 3   positive

4, 5, 6   negative

(See **Integral Combo Five**)

$\sqrt{}$ **RADICAL RULES:**   **Order of Operations: OR BEDMAS**

1. Do the operations with grouping symbols
   i.e. **B**rackets first ( ), [ ], $\dfrac{x}{y}$

2. Do **E**xponents (power) or roots
   i.e. x^2, or $\sqrt{x}$

3. **D**ivide or **M**ultiply in order from left to right

4. **A**dd or **S**ubtract from left to right

BEDMAS MADE EASY!

COMBO SNAP

LEVEL: Grade 7 and up

SKILLS: Order of operations (+, -, x, ÷), problem solving

PLAYERS: 2 or more

EQUIPMENT: Cards Ace - King (Ace = 1, Jack = 11, Queen = 12, King = 0), one decadie

GETTING STARTED: All players build a five by five card grid with twenty-five random cards, face up. The goal of the game is for each player to remove all the cards from their grid. To begin, one player rolls the decadie for all players to use. Players now look for any five card combination that equals the target number rolled (all operations may be used). The first player to pick up a combination says "Combo Snap" and all other players must stop. The player who called out, now verbalizes their five card combination math sentence (e.g. if the decadie equals 50, players might take the following cards to create: 5 x 9 - 4 + 11 - 2 = 50). If they successfully targeted the die, that player now places their five cards aside to begin their point pile. If that player makes an error and their combination does not equal the target number, those cards are replaced into their grid and the other players now resume the play. The player who made an error is disqualified until a new number is rolled. When a combination has successfully been removed from one player's grid, a new number is rolled on the decadie. Play continues until one player removes all of their cards.

 **TEACHING TIP:** Players may want to pay close attention to the numbers on the cards they leave behind. Your last five cards are crucial to the success of the game. For instance, if you are left with the following cards and the target rolled equals a high number, it would be very difficult to equal the target.

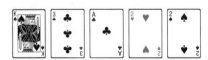

SUPER STAR TRAVELLER

LEVEL: Grade 6 - 9

SKILLS: Order of operations, exponents, square roots, problem solving

PLAYERS: Cooperative groups, pairs or solitaire

EQUIPMENT: Cards Ace - King + 1 Joker (Ace = 1, Jack = 11, Queen = 12, King = 0), two ten-sided (0-9) dice

GETTING STARTED: Players build a 7x7 grid with cards face up. The object of the game is for the group, pair or individual to take away all of the cards before getting all five points of a star coloured in.

EXAMPLE:

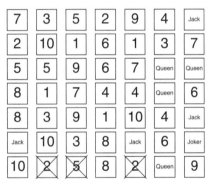

Player rolls the dice and adds them together. Players may take away any card or combination of cards that equals the roll and that appears at the bottom of any column. Addition, subtraction, multiplication, division, or a combination may be used to a maximum of five cards used per roll.

Some sample play:

Roll 5 + 4 = 9

Looking at the bottom row, players could remove 2 + 5 + 2 or go up the second column from the left with 2 + 10 - 3. Once players decide on the combination of cards to be removed, they are taken off, and the dice are rolled again.

Second Roll 2 + 1 = 3

Jack (11) and eight are removed.

etc.

In the event that a card or combination cannot be found, players shade in one point of their star. Play continues until all cards are removed or their star is filled in. As players have more experience, they will develop more strategies to maximize their chances.

VARIATION I: Allow players to remove up to eight cards per roll.

VARIATION II: Players choose any operation before they roll. Players must now use that operation at least once in their combination while reaching their target.

GOT IT / CLOSEST TO!

LEVEL: Grade 6 - 9

SKILLS: Mixed operations (+, -, x, ÷), order of operations, exponents

PLAYERS: Teams of 2 vs. 2, equal skill level

EQUIPMENT: One decadie, two ten-sided (0-9) dice, two regular dice, gameboard (see reproducibles), pencil

GETTING STARTED: All five dice are rolled and set before the two teams. Players are not allowed to touch the dice once they are rolled. The goal of the teams is to target the number on the decadie using the four remaining dice. All remaining dice must be used once.

EXAMPLE: The dice are rolled: ←— Target Decadie

Dice for targeting —→ the decadie

Team One says "Got It" as they calculated an exact bullseye: (5 + 5) x (4 - 3) = 10. Team One now records their math.

There will be roll combinations that cannot be calculated to a bullseye. In this case, a team may call "Closest To", verbalize their sentence and record their math.

EXAMPLE: The dice are rolled: ←— Target Decadie

Dice for targeting —→ the decadie

Team Two says "Closest To".

$8^2 - 1 - 1 = 62$

81

The team who calls out first and correctly gives an answer earns 5 points unless the other team's equation is closer.

In the event a team calls out first and then gives an incorrect response, their opponents now have the opportunity to give either a "Got It" or "Closest To" response and potentially earn 5 points. A team earns 10 points for bullseyeing the target (see sample).

The dice are re-rolled for the next round. Play continues until one team earns 100 points.

TEACHING TIP: This game can be played non-competitively. Each team separately records their own math and then compare their answers. The team <u>closest to</u> the target number would earn the points. If both teams "got it", they would both earn points.

Got it! / Closest TO!

You Need:
1 Decadie (TARGET ROLL)
2 10-SIDED (0-9)
2 Regular Dice

ADVANCE
7-3

	TARGET :	NUMBERS :	EVALUATE :	
1.	90	3,5,4,6	$4^3 + (5 \times 6) = 94$	5
2.	90	4, 6, 6, 2	$(6 + 6 - 2) \times 4 = 40$	10
3.	10	2, 3, 5, 2	$2^3 + 5 - 2 = 11$	5
4.	50	5, 4, 3, 2	$3^2 \times 5 + 4 = 49$	5
5.	60	3, 3, 5, 1	$(3 + 1) \times 5 \times 3 = 60$	
6.	0	7, 4, 1, 8		
7.				

KID'S COMMENTS: This game helped me analyze different combinations of numbers when trying to reach the target. We also had to review the rules for the order of operations because we forgot how! It makes a difference in getting to the right answer.

COMMIT AND CAPTURE

LEVEL: Grade 7 and up

SKILLS: Evaluating equations, order of operations

PLAYERS: 2

EQUIPMENT: Cards Ace - King (Ace = 1, Jack = 11, Queen = 12, King = 0), gameboard (see reproducibles), pencil, calculator (optional for checking only)

GETTING STARTED: The goal of the game is to evaluate your equation for the greatest possible answer and to calculate your opponent's equation for the greatest possible answer and capture it.

This is a two step game. Both players have their own gameboard (but both players must use identical equations, i.e. the same gameboard).

Sample Gameboard: ☐ + ☐ x ☐ ÷ ☐ =

STEP ONE:

Both players take four cards from the top of their deck and begin to calculate the greatest possible answer using the numbers. Once players place their cards onto their gameboard these cards are now "committed" and cannot be rearranged in any other order. Once all four cards have been placed, players record their numbers (in the order placed), evaluate their equation and record this answer as their score.

EXAMPLE:

SCORE

Player One's cards: 5, 9, 6, 3 $5 + 9 \times 6 \div 3 = 23$

Player Two's cards: 11, 6, 9, 1 $11 + 6 \times 9 \div 1 = 65$

NOTE: Players could have placed them into any position.

STEP TWO:

Once both players have finished and recorded their equations the CAPTURING part of the game begins. Players exchange cards and evaluate this new set. If the player can evaluate their opponent's set to create a greater answer than their opponent did, they can now capture this "score" and add it to their own score for that round. If they equal or are less than their opponent's answer no extra (additional) points are earned.

EXAMPLE:

The "Capture" Round:

Player One takes Player Two's cards and records:

$$6 + 11 \times 9 \div 1 =$$
$$6 + 99 \div 1 =$$
$$6 + 99 = 105$$

Since 105 is greater than the score Player Two evaluated (of 65), Player One will also get to add 105 to their own score of 23 for an accumulative score of 128, in the first round (see student sample).

Player Two takes Player One's cards and records:

$$5 + 6 \times 9 \div 3 =$$
$$5 + 54 \div 3 =$$
$$5 + 18 = 23$$

Since 23 was also Player One's score, Player Two does not earn any extra points for that round.

Play continues for a set number of rounds. The player with the highest accumulative score is the winner.

 TEACHING TIP:

See reproducibles for sample gameboards. Have students generate new gameboards that they can use for future rounds of play.

$$\left(\ \boxed{} - \boxed{} \ \right)^{2} \times \ \boxed{} - \boxed{} \ =$$

Record Your Numbers:	Evaluate:	Score:
1. 4 , 6 , 11 , 2	$(11-2)^2 \times 4 - 6 = 318$	318
3 , 1 , 7 , 8	$(8-1)^2 \times 3 - 7 = 140$	+ 0
2. 12 , 3 , 8 , 1	$(12-1)^2 \times 8 - 3 = 965$	965
6 , 6 , 7 , 2	$(7-2)^2 \times 6 - 6 = 144$	+ 144
3. 3 , 8 , 5 , 7	$(7-3)^2 \times 8 - 5 = 123$	123
12 , 2 , 7 , 6	$(12-2)^2 \times 7 - 6 = 694$	+ 0
4. 2 , 9 , 9 , 4	$(9-2)^2 \times 9 - 4 = 437$	437
1 , 0 , 11 , 9	$(11-0)^2 \times 9 - 1 = 1088$	+ 0
5. 7 , 10 , 3 , 1	$(10-1)^2 \times 7 - 3 = 564$	564
10 , 8 , 2 , 5	$(10-2)^2 \times 8 - 5 = 507$	+ 507

Total = 3058

BALANCING ACT

LEVEL: Grade 7 - 9

SKILLS: Order of operations, creating a balanced equation

PLAYERS: Teams: 2 vs. 2

EQUIPMENT: One thirty-sided (1-30) die, paper, pencil

GETTING STARTED: The goal of the game is to be the first team to create a balanced equation with a minimum of four numbers and at least two different operations.

Play begins by selecting one player to be the roller for the round. This player will roll the numbers that each team will record and use. All numbers rolled do <u>not</u> have to be used when players are creating their equations, however the equation must have the minimum of four. Each number rolled can only be used once in the equation. If any number is rolled more than once (e.g. two 8's are rolled), both numbers are recorded and can potentially be used. As the numbers are rolled, both teams record them and begin to calculate potentially balanced equations. The roller must provide adequate time between rolls to allow both teams enough time to evaluate possible combinations for creating a balanced equation.

EXAMPLE: **Team One's Play Only:**

Rolls: 8, 30, 8, 20, 19

Team One verbalizes "STOP!" and now shows their opponents their recorded balanced equation.

$8 \div 8 = 20 - 19$

To score, players earn 1 point for each number used in their equation (e.g. Team One scores 4 points for the above equation). A new round begins by selecting a new roller who generates a new set of numbers.

Play continues for a set period of time. The team with the most points earned wins.

VARIATIONS: Any number rolled can be used as a negative value. Players may also use the numbers rolled as exponents. Square roots and fractions can also be worked into the equation.

Exponents
and Radicals

EXPONENT WAR

LEVEL: Grade 7 - 10

SKILLS: Multiplication (exponents), with positive and negative integers

PLAYERS: 2

EQUIPMENT: Cards Ace - 5 (Ace = 1) or Ace - 9 (Ace = 1) for advanced players

GETTING STARTED: Players divide the cards evenly between themselves. Players turn over two cards each. Black cards are positive and red cards are negative. The first card turned up is the base card and the second card is the exponent. Example: Player One turns up a 3 and then a 4. The total is 3 x 3 x 3 x 3 = 81. The player with the highest total wins all four cards. Play continues until one player earns all of the cards. In the event of a tie (i.e. both players have the same totals), each player deals three cards face down. Two more cards are turned face up in the same manner as above and the higher total wins all of the cards.

EXAMPLE:

Player One	Player Two
red 2, black 4	black 4, black 2
$(-2)^4 = (-2) \times (-2) \times (-2) \times (-2)$	$4^2 = 4 \times 4$
$= 16$	$= 16$
–	–
– {three cards	–
– face down}	–
red 3, black 5	red 1, black 4
$= (-3) \times (-3) \times (-3) \times (-3) \times (-3)$	$= (-1) \times (-1) \times (-1) \times (-1)$
$= -243$	$= 1$

Player Two would collect all of the cards.

√ RADICAL RULES: A power is a number with a base and an exponent (e.g. 3^4 - 3 is the base and 4 is the exponent). When you use an exponent, the base is a repeated factor and the exponent determines the number of times the base is used as a factor.

EXAMPLE: $3^4 = 3 \times 3 \times 3 \times 3$

POWER TO YA!

LEVEL: Grade 7 - 10

SKILLS: Multiplication (exponents), with positive and negative integers

Variation: order of operation

PLAYERS: 2 of equal skill level

EQUIPMENT: Cards Ace - 5 (Ace = 1) or Ace - 9 (Ace = 1) for advanced players (calculators to check for accuracy)

GETTING STARTED: Players divide the cards evenly between themselves. Each player turns over one card at the same time. Black cards are positive and red cards are negative. One player continuously turns over the base card while the other turns over the exponent card. The first player to say the correct answer out loud collects both cards. Play continues until one player collects all of the cards.

In the event of a tie, the two cards are left face down in a pile and two more cards are turned over until one player gives the correct answer before the other and collects all of the cards.

EXAMPLE:

Player One (base)	Player Two (exponent)
black 4 (+4)	red 3 (-3)

Correct Answer $= 4^{-3} = \dfrac{1}{4^3} = \dfrac{1}{64}$

VARIATION: To increase the level of difficulty each player could turn over two cards and build a number just as above. Players now race to multiply these two numbers together and the first player to verbalize the correct product earns the cards.

EXAMPLE:

Player One	Player Two
(+3) (+3)	(-5) (+2)

$3^3 \times -5^2 = 27 \times 25 = 675$

Player Two verbalizes "six hundred seventy-five" first and earns all the cards.

EXPRESSION WAR

LEVEL: Grade 9 - 10

SKILLS: Substitution into an algebraic expression, order of operations, exponent laws

PLAYERS: 2 to 4

EQUIPMENT: Two ten-sided (0-9) dice, calculator (optional), one regular die, paper, pencil

GETTING STARTED: Each player creates a one termed expression using coefficients, variables and exponents. One, two, three or four numbers are rolled using the ten-sided (0-9) die to determine the values of the variables. Prior to rolling, players may choose to designate the number rolled as either positive or negative. The number of times the die is rolled depends on how many variables there are in the expression. Each player now substitutes these values in and evaluates their expression. The regular die is now rolled to determine who receives the point for the round:

        1, 2, 3 (least rolls)   lowest value wins

        4, 5, 6 (greatest rolls)   highest value wins

The first player to earn 10 points wins.

EXAMPLE:

Player One	Player Two	Player Three
$4x^2y$	$-10ab^3$	$5d^4$

Two numbers are rolled: **3**   **6**   (+3, -6)

NOTE: Player Three would use only +3 since it was the first number rolled.

Player One	Player Two	Player Three
$4(3)^2(-6)$	$-10(3)(-6)^3$	$5(3)^4$
$4(9)(-6)$	$-10(3)(-216)$	$5(81)$
-216	$6\ 480$	405

Roll 3 therefore least amount wins.
Player One gets the point.

VARIATION: Players may agree on the number of variables that are used in the expression or that the expression must be of a certain degree.

SIMPLY RADICAL

(submitted by Cheri Eck)

LEVEL: Grade 8 - 11

SKILLS: Simplifying radicals, factoring

PLAYERS: 2 of equal skill level

EQUIPMENT: Two twenty-sided (1-20) dice, calculators, paper, pencil

GETTING STARTED: Each player rolls a twenty-sided die. At the same time players multiply the two numbers and find the square root in simplified mixed form. The first player to verbalize the correct answer out loud earns the point.

EXAMPLE: Numbers rolled: 15 and 5

$$\sqrt{75} = \sqrt{25 \times 3} \qquad \sqrt{25} = 5\sqrt{3}$$

Numbers rolled: 18 and 12

$$18 \times 12 = 216$$

$$\sqrt{216} = \sqrt{9 \times 2 \times 4 \times 3} = \sqrt{9 \times 4}\sqrt{2 \times 3} =$$

$$\sqrt{36}\sqrt{6} = 6\sqrt{6}$$

Play continues for a set period of time. The player with the most points is the winner.

BE RATIONAL!

(submitted by Cheri Eck)

LEVEL: Grade 8 - 11

SKILLS: Rationalizing denominators of radical expressions and simplifying.

PLAYERS: 2 - 4

EQUIPMENT: Cards Ace - King (Ace = 1, Jack = 11, Queen = 12, King = 0), paper, pencil

GETTING STARTED: Each student draws three cards and arranges them on their gameboard. Each student then rationalizes and simplifies their expression. Students share their original and simplified expression. If they are correct, they add the numbers in their simplified answer and receive that many points. If their answer is incorrect the student who says "be rational" first may correct the answer and steal that player's points.

EXAMPLE: Player One:

11, Queen, 5

$$\frac{Queen\,(12)}{\sqrt{11}+5} = \frac{12\,(\sqrt{11}-5)}{(\sqrt{11}+5)(\sqrt{11}-5)} = \frac{12\sqrt{11}-60}{11-25} =$$

$$\frac{12\sqrt{11}-60}{-14} = \frac{30-6\sqrt{11}}{7}$$

Points earned = 30 + 6 + 11 + 7 = 54

Play continues for a set period until one player reaches 500 points.

Polynomials and their Operations

RADICAL ROOTS

LEVEL: Grade 9 and up

SKILLS: Finding square roots of whole numbers, problem solving

PLAYERS: 2 of equal skill level

EQUIPMENT: Cards King - 9 (King = 0, Ace = 1), one calculator per player, paper, pencil

GETTING STARTED: The goal of the game is to be the first player to find the exact square root of the six-digit number (or closest to without going over). To begin, players determine who will deal six cards off the top of the deck. Players now record these six numbers in the order they were drawn from left to right on their paper and begin to extract the square root of this number.

EXAMPLE: Cards: 4, 1, 2, 1, 6, 4

Player One's Work Only

Players record $\sqrt{412164}$ and begin to extract the square root.

TEACHING TIP: Have players start at the right, and divide the number into groups of two digits each. In the answer there will be one digit for each group. Now find the largest number which, when squared, is contained in the first left hand group of digits (e.g. 41). In this example, 6 is the number (6 x 6 = 36 - the closest number to 41). Players now know that 6 will be the first digit in their square root answer.

Once the mental math has been done to determine the first number of the possible square root, the players now use their calculators to find the exact or closest to square root.

Players race by plugging into their calculators possible square root solutions.

EXAMPLE: **Player One:** 650 x 650 = 422 500 -> too big
                             630 x 630 = 396 900 -> too small
                             640 x 640 = 409 600 -> getting closer
                             642 x 642 = EXACT

Player One verbalizes 642 is the exact square root and earns all of the cards.

Players check their answers:

642 x 642 = 412 164

In the event an exact square root can not be found for any six-digit number using the cards, the first player to verbalize the closest number without going over the six-digit number earns a point and six new cards are drawn for the next round.

Play continues for a set period of time. The player with the most points wins.

POLY WANT A NUMBER!

LEVEL:	Grade 9 and up
SKILLS:	Adding binomial polynomials, recognition of polynomials, combining like terms to simplify expressions, substitution and order of operations
PLAYERS:	2 - 4
EQUIPMENT:	Cards Ace - King (Ace = 1, Jack = 11, Queen = 12, King = 0), one twelve-sided (1-12) die, one regular die, paper, pencil
GETTING STARTED:	To begin, each player rolls the regular die which indicates the number of cards they are dealt from the top of the deck. If a 1 is rolled on the die, players must re-roll for a new number.

Player One rolls a 2 on the regular die and now draws two cards off the deck.

Player Two rolls a 4 and draws four cards off the deck.

Red cards are negative values and black are positive. As players arrange their cards from left to right, they must remember that the first, third and fifth cards are always the coefficient of the variable (x). Therefore the second, fourth and sixth cards represent number values (the constants in the expression).

Players can choose to place their cards in any order, but once set, they cannot be moved.

EXAMPLE: Player One Roll: Player Two Roll:

$$\boxed{5}\, x +\boxed{2} \qquad \boxed{1}\, x +\boxed{8} +\boxed{3}\, x +\boxed{7}$$

B   R   B   R   B   B

Players now alternate rolling the twelve-sided (1-12) die and this number is substituted into their polynomials (i.e. the variable x).

Roll = 3

Player One	Player Two
5x + -2	1x + -8 + 3x + 7
5(3) + -2	4x – 1
15 + -2	4(3) – 1
13	12 – 1
	11

Player One now verbalizes "thirteen is greater than eleven" and earns all of the cards. Play continues for a set period of time. The player with the most cards wins.

√ **RADICAL RULES:**   When you combine like terms or use properties (i.e. commutative, associative and distributive) to make polynomial expressions less difficult to work with, you are <u>simplifying</u>.

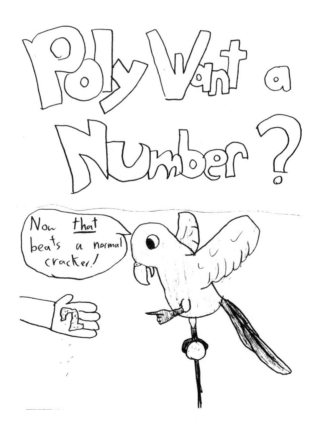

POLY SUBTRACTION WAR

LEVEL: Grade 9 and up

SKILLS: Subtracting polynomials, recognition of polynomials, combining like terms to simplify expressions, substitution and order of operations

PLAYERS: 2 - 4

EQUIPMENT: Cards Ace - King (Ace = 1, Jack = 11, Queen = 12, King = 0), one twelve-sided (1-12) die, one regular die, paper, pencil

GETTING STARTED: The goal of the game is to have the least number after evaluating a polynomial. To begin, each player rolls the regular die which indicates the number of cards they are dealt from the top of the deck. If a 1 is rolled on the die, players must re-roll for a new number. Red cards are negative values and black are positive.

Player One rolls: and takes three cards

Player Two rolls: (re-rolls), rolls

Player Two takes four cards

As players arrange their cards from left to right they must remember that the first, third and fifth cards are always the coefficient of the variable (x). Thus the second, fourth and sixth cards represent number values (the constants in the expression).

EXAMPLE:

Player One Rolls:	**Player Two Rolls:**

Re-rolls:

$$\boxed{1}x - \boxed{8} - \boxed{5}x \qquad \boxed{11}x - \boxed{6} - \boxed{4}x - \boxed{1}$$

R   B   B   B   R   R   B

Players now alternate rolling the twelve-sided (1-12) die and this number is substituted into their polynomials (i.e. the variable x).

Roll =

Player One	Player Two
-1x − 8 − 5x	11x − -6 − -4x − 1
-6x − 8	15x − -7
-6(6) − 8	15(6) − -7
-36 − 8	90 + 7
-44	97

Player One now verbalizes "negative forty-four is less than ninety-seven" and earns all of the cards. Play continues for a set period of time. The player with the most cards wins.

√ **RADICAL RULES:**

To combine like terms you need to group all the added terms in degree order: squared variable, variable with no exponent, no variable.

BINOMIAL CROSS OVERS

LEVEL: Grade 9 and up

SKILLS: Adding and subtracting polynomials, recognition of polynomials

PLAYERS: 2 - 4

EQUIPMENT: One twelve-sided (1-12) die per player, one gameboard per player (see reproducibles), paper, pencil

GETTING STARTED: The goal of the game is to be the first player to eliminate (cross off) five consecutive numbers in a row on their number line. Both players work with the same gameboard.

$$(\Box x + \Box) + (\Box x + \Box)$$

To begin, Player One rolls their twelve-sided (1-12) die four times and chooses to record their numbers in any order into their polynomial.

EXAMPLE: **Player One rolls:** 2, 11, 5, 4

Player One records and simplifies the following polynomial:

$(2x + 11) + (4x + 5)$
$6x + 16$

Player One now crosses off both 6 and 16 on their number line, as these are their simplified values. Players can also choose to record any of their numbers as a positive or negative value.

Player Two rolls: 7, 16, 3, 12

Player Two records the following polynomial:

$(12x - 7) + (3x + 16)$
$15x + 9$

Player Two now crosses off both 15 and 9 on their number line.

Play continues until one player has successfully crossed off five consecutive numbers on their gameboard.

VARIATION I: Play binomial cross overs using the subtraction gameboard: $(\Box x - \Box) - (\Box x - \Box)$

VARIATION II: Make the gameboard more difficult by using two trinomials.

SNAPPY BINOMIALS

LEVEL: Grade 10 and up

SKILLS: Factoring binomials
Variation: factoring trinomials

PLAYERS: 2 of equal skill level

EQUIPMENT: Cards Ace - King (Ace = 1, Jack = 11, Queen = 12, King = 0), paper, pencil

GETTING STARTED: The goal of the game is to be the first player to create a binomial, factor it and verbalize it correctly out loud.

To begin, players determine who will be the card dealer for that round. One player flips up six cards for both players to see. These cards are not to be taken by either player, as they are for both players to use. Two cards can be combined to make a two-digit number (e.g. 2 and 5 = 25), however, each card can only be used once in any combination.

Players now race to record a binomial using some of the numbers indicated on the cards. Players are also racing to factor the binomial and verbalize it out loud before their opponent. The player who correctly verbalizes their factored polynomial earns all of the cards.

In the event that a binomial can not be factored by using any of the numbers on the six cards, the first player to verbalize "Not Factorable" earns all of the cards. If players tie (i.e. verbalize their answers at the same time), no cards are earned.

EXAMPLE: Cards: 5, 8, 2, King, 4, 5

Player One Records: $8a^2x^2 + 4a^3x$
$$= 4a^2x \, (\, 2x + a \,)$$

NOTE: $4a^2x$ is a factor common to both terms.

Since Player One is correct, and was the first player to finish, they earn all of the cards.

NOTE: Player One could have also recorded $8x + 4 = 4(2x + 1)$ and their answer would have also been correct.

Other possible solutions include:

1. $5x - 25x^2 = 5x (1 - 5x)$

2. $4a^2bc^3 - 28abc = 4abc (ac^2 - 7)$

3. $4a^4b^3 + 2a^3b = 2a^3b (2ab^2 + 1)$

$\sqrt{\text{RADICAL RULES:}}$ Factoring is the process of separating a quantity into factors. If every term of a polynomial contains the same monomial factor, then that monomial is one factor of the polynomial and the other factor is equal to the quotient of the polynomial divided by the monomial factor.

VARIATION: Play as above but now players create and factor trinomials. Players factor trinomials when the coefficient of the squared term equals 1.

EXAMPLE: $x^2 + 10x + 24 = (x + 6)(x + 4)$

Players look for two numbers whose product is 24 and whose sum is 10.

EXAMPLE: Cards: 5, 4, 8, 2, 1, 6

Possible Solutions:

1. $x^2 + 5x - 24 = (x + 8)(x - 3)$

2. $x^2 - 16x + 28 = (x - 14)(x - 2)$

DON'T BE FOILED!

LEVEL: Grade 9 and up

SKILLS: Multiplying binomial polynomials, substitution, evaluation and order of operations

PLAYERS: 2

EQUIPMENT: One twelve-sided (1-12) die per player, paper, pencil

GETTING STARTED: The goal of the game is to be the player with the highest product. To begin, both players need to copy down the following polynomial:

$$(\underline{\quad}x + \underline{\quad}) (\underline{\quad}x - \underline{\quad})$$

Players alternate rolling their twelve-sided (1-12) die and after each roll, players record their numbers into their polynomial gameboards from left to right. Each player now calculates the product of their binomials by combining like terms.

EXAMPLE:

Player One:
$$(8x + 6) (x - 4)$$
$$= 8x^2 + \text{-}32x + 6x - 24$$
$$= 8x^2 - 26x - 24$$

Player Two:
$$(9x + 7) (x - 9)$$
$$= 9x^2 + \text{-}81x + 7x - 63$$
$$= 9x^2 - 74x - 63$$

One player now rolls the twelve-sided (1-12) die for both players to use and this number is substituted in for x.

Roll = 3

Player One:
$$8(3)^2 + \text{-}26(3) - 24$$
$$= 576 - 78 - 24$$
$$= 474$$

Player Two:
$$9(3)^2 - 74(3) - 63$$
$$= 729 - 222 - 63$$
$$= 444$$

Since four hundred seventy-four is greater than four hundred forty-four, Player One wins the first round and scores 5 points.

Play continues for a set period of time. The player with the most points wins.

VARIATION I: Use cards K - 12 (King = 0, Ace = 1, Jack = 11, Queen = 12). Red cards are negative values and black cards are positive. Players are dealt four cards each and create two linear binomials and calculate their product. A separate, additional card is then drawn from the top of the deck and this new number is substituted into each player's polynomial. the player with the greatest value earns all of the cards.

VARIATION II: After players have completed all calculations, one player rolls the twelve-sided (1-12) die to determine who earns the points. If an even number is rolled (i.e. 2, 4, 6, 8, 10 or 12), the player with the greatest product earns the points. If it is an odd number (i.e. 1, 3, 5, 7, 9 or 11), the player with the least product earns the points.

$\sqrt{\text{RADICAL RULES:}}$ **Understanding FOIL**

FOIL stands for multiplying

1.   First term by **F**irst term

2.   **O**uter term by Outer term (outside edges)

3.   **I**nside term by Inside term (the middle guys)

4.   Last term by **L**ast term

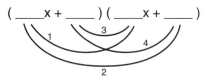

BOUNCY BINOMIALS

LEVEL: Grade 9 and up

SKILLS: Multiplying binomials, recognition of polynomials, substitution, order of operations

PLAYERS: 2 - 4

EQUIPMENT: Cards Ace - King (Ace = 1, Jack = 11, Queen = 12, King = 0), one regular die, paper, pencil

GETTING STARTED: The goal of the game is to be the player with the greatest product. Before actual play begins, all players must copy the following gameboard on their paper:

$$(\underline{\quad} x + \underline{\quad}) (\underline{\quad} x + \underline{\quad})$$

Each player now draws four cards off the top of the deck. These cards can now be manipulated to create two linear binomials. Red cards are negative values and black cards are positive. Each player calculates the product of their own binomial.

Player One	Player Two
+4, +1, +12, -5	-7, 0, 3, -11
$(4x + 1)(12x - 5)$	$(-7x)(3x - 11)$
$48x^2 - 20x + 12x - 5$	$-21x^2 + 77x$
$48x^2 - 8x - 5$	

To determine who earns the cards for the round, one player draws a new card off the top of the deck for all players to use (remember: red = negative and black = positive). Players now substitute this number into their own polynomials and the player with the highest value earns all of the cards.

Player One	Player Two
$48(-5)^2 - 8(-5) - 5$	$-21(-5)^2 + 77(-5)$
$1\,200 - (-40) - 5$	$-525 - 385$
$1\,235$	-910

Player One verbalizes "one thousand two hundred and thirty-five is greater than negative nine hundred and ten" and earns all of the cards.

VARIATION: Play fair-game multiplication of polynomials. After both players have substituted in the value indicated on the last card drawn, the regular die is rolled.

If an odd number is rolled (i.e. 1, 3 or 5) the player with the least product earns all of the cards. If an even number is rolled (i.e. 2, 4 or 6) the player with the highest product earns all of the cards. Play continues for a set period of time. The player with the most cards wins.

√ RADICAL RULES:

When multiplying binomials use the shortcut: FOIL

Multiply the First terms, then the Outer terms, then the Inner terms and finally the Last terms.

PREDICTING THE FACTS WITH POLLY

LEVEL: Grade 10 and up

SKILLS: Predicting, factoring quadratic polynomials

PLAYERS: 2 - 4 of equal skill level

EQUIPMENT: One twenty-sided (1-20) die, paper, pencil

GETTING STARTED: The object of the game is to correctly predict whether the polynomial can be factored and if so, factor it correctly for additional points. Players alternate being the roller for each round.

Play begins by one player rolling the twenty-sided (1-20) die five times. Players will be selecting a minimum of three numbers to use when building their polynomial.

Each player now records a yes or no on their paper indicating whether they predict that these numbers can generate a polynomial that can be factored. Now all players record any possible solutions for a polynomial and attempt to factor it.

EXAMPLE: Rolls: 9, 18, 1, 7, 13

Prediction: yes it is factorable

Player One selects: 9, 18, 1

$x^2 + 9x + 18$
$(x + 3) (x + 6)$

Check:

$x^2 + 6x + 3x + 18$
$x^2 + 9x + 18$

Since Player One predicted correctly, they earn 1 point. They earn 2 additional points for factoring this polynomial correctly.

VARIATION I: Increase the level of difficulty by having all even numbers rolled as positive values (i.e. 2, 4, 6... 20) and all odd numbers rolled as negative values (i.e. 1, 3, 5... 19).

VARIATION II: Decrease the level of difficulty by having players only roll two numbers and thereby only creating polynomials with 1 as the leading coefficient (as in the example above).

√‾‾‾‾‾‾‾‾‾‾
RADICAL RULES: If a trinomial has the form $x^2 + 6x + c$ and is factorable into two binomial factors, the first term of each factor will be x; the second term of the binomial will be two numbers whose product is c and whose sum is equal to b, which is the coefficient of the middle term of the trinomial.

POLYS AND PROBABILITY

LEVEL: Grade 9 - 11

SKILLS: Probability, recognizing and applying the terms: coefficient, term, degree, monomial, binomial, trinomial, polynomial, order of operations, substitution and evaluating polynomials

PLAYERS: 2

EQUIPMENT: Cards Ace - 5 (Ace = 1), paper, pencil

GETTING STARTED: The goal of the game is to be the player with the highest valued polynomial. To begin, each player draws a card off the deck and must decide if they want that number to determine the degree, the number of variables or number of terms for their polynomial.

STEP ONE: Player flips up a 5 and decides: FIVE TERMS

Each player now draws their second card off the deck and must decide if they want that number to determine the remaining constraints (e.g. if the player chose terms already, they now can only choose degree or variables).

STEP TWO: Player flips up a 2 and decides: TWO DEGREES

Each player now draws their third card off the deck and this number will determine whichever constraint is left.

STEP THREE: Player flips up a 3 and this must determine the number of variables: THREE VARIABLES

Each player now creates a polynomial given their constraints.

EXAMPLE: **Player One's work only:**

$x^2 - xy + z + xy + z^2$

Players now draw new cards one at a time (red cards are negative values, black cards are positive) and try to create the highest number after evaluating their polynomial. Since Player One in the above example has three variables, only three cards will be drawn. As each card is drawn, the player must decide which variable this number will be substituted in for.

EXAMPLE:

Player One draws a black 4 and decides x = 4. Player One then draws a black 1 and decides y = 1 and lastly, Player One draws a red 3 and z = -3.

Player One now evaluates their polynomial.

$$4^2 - 4(1) + -3 + 4(1) + (-3)^2$$
$$= 16 - 4 + -3 + 4 + 9$$
$$= 22$$

Player One now compares their answer with Player Two and the player with the greatest answer earns 5 points. Play continues until one player earns 25 points.

VARIATION I:

Have players change the goal of the game so the player with the least valued polynomial earns the points.

VARIATION II:

Have students play in teams of two. The team with the most points wins.

Linear

Equations

INSPECTOR "X"

LEVEL: Grade 8 - 10

SKILLS: Solving linear equations

PLAYERS: 2 of equal skill level

EQUIPMENT: Cards Ace - King (Ace = 1, Jack = 11, Queen = 12, King = 0), calculators (for checking answers only), paper, pencil

GETTING STARTED: The goal of the game is to be the player with the highest result. To begin, both players must record the following gameboard to work with throughout the game:

$$\Box x + \Box = \Box$$

Each player now draws three cards from the top of the deck. Players now manipulate their cards to create a linear equation, using their gameboard.

Player One's Cards	Player Two's Cards
2, 11, 1	6, 3, 12
Player One chooses and records:	Player Two chooses and records:

$2x + 1 = 11$	$3x + 6 = 12$
$2x = 11 - 1$	$3x = 6$
$2x = 10$	$x = 2$
$x = 5$	

Player One has the greater result and earns 1 point. Play continues for a set period of time. The player with the most points wins.

VARIATION I: Players can choose from the following gameboards in future rounds of play:

1. $\Box x = \Box$ 2. $\Box x + \Box = \Box x + \Box$

3. $\Box = \Box x + \Box$ 4. $\Box x + \Box = \Box x$

VARIATION II: Players assign black cards as positive values and red cards as negative.

√‾RADICAL RULES: The graph for any linear equation is a straight line. Since two points define a line, you only need to find two points to graph a line. To find two points to plot, first you need to simplify the equation, then substitute in a value for x and solve for y.

EQUATING SNAP

LEVEL: Grade 9 and up

SKILLS: Solving linear equations

PLAYERS: 2 of equal skill level

EQUIPMENT: Cards Ace - King (Ace = 1, Jack = 11, Queen = 12, King = 0), paper, pencil

GETTING STARTED: The goal of the game is to be the first player to correctly verbalize the value of x. To begin, both players must record the following gameboard to work with throughout the game:

$$\Box = \Box x + \Box$$

Players alternate being the card dealer for consecutive rounds of play. The three cards drawn will be used by both players. Each player records these numbers and begins to manipulate them in an attempt to come up with the highest value for x. The first player to correctly verbalize the highest value for x, earns 1 point.

EXAMPLE: **Player One draws:** 3, 5, 1

$$5 = 1x + 3$$
$$2 = 1x$$
$$2 = x$$

Player Two verbalizes the answer first and scores 1 point.

VARIATION I: Players can choose from the following gameboards for future rounds of play:

1. $\Box x = \Box$

2. $\Box x + \Box = \Box x + \Box$

3. $\Box = \Box x + \Box$

4. $\Box x + \Box = \Box x$

VARIATION II: Players assign black cards as positive values and red cards as negative.

$\sqrt{\;}$ **RADICAL RULES:** In a linear function, a change in x causes proportional change in y. Thus, if you double x, you double y.

GIVE ME FIVE

LEVEL: Grade 9 and up

SKILLS: Solving linear equations

PLAYERS: 2 cooperative teams of 2 vs. 2 or 3 vs. 3

EQUIPMENT: One twelve-sided (1-12) die, one twenty-sided (1-20) die and one thirty-sided (1-30) die per team, one hundred board per team (see reproducibles), bingo chips or other counters, paper, pencil

GETTING STARTED: The goal of the game is to be the first team to cover five numbers in a row, in any direction on their hundred board (vertically, horizontally or diagonally).

To begin, Team One rolls all three dice and finds the solutions to the following linear equations by substituting in the values of the numbers rolled.

1. $\square x + \square = \square$

2. $\square x + \square = \square x$

3. $x + \square = \square$

While Team One is calculating all solutions and marking their hundred board, Team Two is checking their answers AND calculating for any possible "missed" solutions. After approximately 3-5 minutes have passed (players must agree prior to the play, how much time is allotted before the opposition says STOP!), the players must then pass the three dice to the other team. Any solutions missed by Team One can now be covered on Team Two's board before Team Two takes their turn. Players must always show their work before placing a chip on their board.

EXAMPLE:

Team One's Play Only:

Team One rolls: 7, 18, 25

Possible Solutions:

1. $x + 18 = 25$
          $x = 7$

    (cover up 7)

2. $x + 7 = 25$
          $x = 18$

    (cover up 18)

3. $7x + 18 = 25x$
        $18 = 18x$
         $1 = x$

    (cover up 1)

4. $25x + 7 = 18$
        $25x = 11$
        $x = \dfrac{11}{25} = .44$

    (cover up 11, 25 and 44)

Team Two now verbalizes "STOP". Since Team One missed the solution:

$$x + 7 = 18$$
$$x = 11$$

Team Two can now cover this number on their hundred board.

Team Two now takes their turn. Play continues until one team successfully covers five numbers in any direction.

 **TEACHING TIP:**   Players on the same team may assign each other specific gameboards to work from, in order to avoid duplicating any answers.

LINEAR KNOCK OFFS

LEVEL: Grade 9 and up

SKILLS: Solving linear equations, problem solving

PLAYERS: 2 to 4

EQUIPMENT: Four thirty-sided (1-30) dice, thirty bingo chips per player (of their own colour), one number line per player (see reproducibles), paper, pencil

GETTING STARTED: The goal of the game is to be the first player to cover up five consecutive numbers on their number line. To begin, Player One rolls all four dice and using the following gameboard, creates and chooses one of the following linear equations (for values of x):

$$\square x + \square = \square x + \square$$

Player One rolls: 4, 22, 16, 10

First solution:
$$4x + 22 = 16x + 10$$
$$12 = 12x$$
$$1 = x$$

Second solution:
$$16x + 4 = 10x + 22$$
$$6x = 18$$
$$x = 3$$

Third solution:
$$22x + 16 = 10x + 4$$
$$12x = -12$$
$$x = -1$$

Fourth solution:
$$16x + 10 = 22x + 4$$
$$-6x = -6$$
$$x = 1$$

Player One decides to stop and now chooses one of their linear equation solutions (e.g. the first solution x = 1). Player One now covers up this number on their number line.

EXAMPLE:

The first player to get five consecutive numbers in a row wins.

121

SOLUTION SEEKERS

LEVEL: Grade 9 and up

SKILLS: Checking solutions (i.e. ordered pairs) to linear equations, substitution, predicting

PLAYERS: 2 - 4

EQUIPMENT: One thirty-sided (1-30) die, one regular die, paper, pencil

GETTING STARTED: The goal of the game is to correctly predict whether an ordered pair lies on the graph of the equation. To begin, all players record the following equation:

$nx + ny = n$

Players alternate rolling in the values for their equation and also, the numbers for the ordered pair.

The first two numbers are rolled using the regular die and are substituted for the values of x and y. The thirty-sided (1-30) die is rolled to substitute in for the sum of the linear equation.

EXAMPLE: Regular dice:

Thirty-sided (1-30) die:

$3x + 4y = 18$

Once the numbers are rolled for the linear equation, each player now rolls the regular die two more times to create an ordered pair.

Players can choose how they wish to set their ordered pair, i.e. (3, 4) or (4, 3), but once set and recorded, this can not be changed.

Each player must now predict out loud whether they think their ordered pair is a solution to their own linear equation. Players record yes or no on their paper and now begin to check and solve. To score, 1 point is earned if a player is correct in predicting that the ordered pair is not a solution. Five points are earned for correctly predicting that the ordered pair is a solution.

EXAMPLE:

Round One:

Player One predicts "yes" - that (3, 4) is an ordered pair that lies on the graph of:

$$5x + 1y = 20$$
$$5(3) + 1(4) = 20$$
$$15 + 4 = 20$$

$$19 \neq 20$$

Since Player One's prediction is incorrect, no points are earned.

Player Two predicts "no" - that (4, 3) is not an ordered pair that lies on the graph of:

$$5x + 1y = 20$$
$$5(4) + 1(3) = 20$$
$$20 + 3 = 20$$

$$23 \neq 20$$

Since Player Two's prediction is correct, they earn 1 point.

Round Two:

Player One predicts "yes" - that (2, 3) is an ordered pair that lies on the graph of:

$$3x + 3y = 15$$
$$3(2) + 3(3) = 15$$
$$6 + 9 = 15$$

$$15 = 15$$

Since Player One's prediction is correct, they earn 5 points.

Player Two predicts "no" - that (2, 3) is not an ordered pair that lies on the graph of $3x + 3y = 15$ and thus, earns no points for this round.

Players continue alternating the rolling throughout fifteen consecutive rounds and the player with the most points wins.

VARIATION: Use different linear equations for players to solve.

EXAMPLE: $y = \dfrac{x}{\square} = \square$

ALGEBRA MATH FOOTBALL

(submitted by Nancy McGuire)

LEVEL: Grade 7 - 10

SKILLS: Solving linear equations, adding binomial polynomials, recognition of polynomials, substitution, problem solving

PLAYERS: 6 of equal ability (2 playing teams of 2 and a Referee team of two)

EQUIPMENT: Football Field (see reproducibles), Football (or some other marker), 5 bingo chips for markers, one thirty-sided (1-30) die, one ten-sided (0-9) die, one twelve-sided (1-12) die or various regular dice of different colours (see variation options)

GETTING STARTED: Players move up and down the playing field in order to score points in a set amount of time. Each of the following variations follow the rules of the basic game. The differences are the mathematical concept being practiced and the particular dice used.

BASIC GAME: Each team lines up on one side of the field. The referee is in the middle. Using a twelve-sided (1-12) die, each team rolls the die to decide who is Home team. The Home team goes first. The ball is placed on the Home team's 20 yard line. The Home team has 4 downs in which to score a goal. The referee puts a bingo chip in the Home's Ball square to show that the Home team has possession of the ball. The teacher chooses a solution to work out (see variations).

Home team rolls the die and each team applies the number rolled as the variable in the solution. The referees decide which team called out the solution first.

EXAMPLE: Solution to be evaluated is $3x + 8$

7 is rolled: $3(7) + 8 = 29$. The first team to call out "29" wins the down.

If the Visitor team calls out the solution first, no yardage is gained and the play moves to second down. If the Home team calls out the solution first, then yardage is gained for the Home team. The thirty-sided (1-30) die is rolled to determine the amount of yardage gained for the home team. If, for example, a 17 is rolled, then a player on the Home team moves the ball 17 yards toward their goal line.

After the result (i.e. progress stopped, or yardage gained) for the first down has been completed, then the referee places another bingo chip in the second down square to signify that it is second down. Play repeats for the second, third, and fourth downs, or until a score is made. If after the fourth down the Home team (the team with possession of the ball) has not scored then the ball turns over right where it is (after the fourth down results have been moved). The Visitor team now takes possession of the ball. The referee moves the possession bingo chip over to the Visitor side, removes the down markers from the previous set of downs, and puts a chip down to signify that it is the Visitor's first down. Play continues as above for 4 downs, or until a touchdown is scored, then the ball changes possession again.

Scoring: 6 points are scored for a touchdown

Extra points: The scoring team has an option to "go for" either 1 or 2 extra points. The team has to tell the opposing team which they are trying for, 1 or 2.

To score 1 point, the team in possession of the ball rolls the dice and must call out the solution before the opposing team, one time.

To score 2 points, the team in possession must call out the solution before the opposing team, twice in a row.

 **TEACHING TIP:** To make teams of equal ability easily, give a one minute fast multiplication test. Correct it together as a class. Then just order the tests from greatest to least and just pick off two at a time to make teams. The refereeing team has to be of equal ability as well. Be aware that this activity gets loud when you have several games going at once, but it is fun to see the kids so into their game that they don't even notice the other games going on at the same time.

Consider having a grade level, lunch time or after school, tournament. Let kids choose team names and make banners and flags. Put kids of varying levels into different divisions (Eastern, Central, and Western) and have a winner for each division. End the tournament with a Math Football Superbowl.

VARIATION II: Roll a regular die, a ten-sided (0-9) die and a twelve-sided (1-12) die. Designate the ten-sided (0-9) die as the value for x and the twelve-sided (1-12) die as the value for y. The regular die represents the multiplier. Dice are rolled, multiplied and added.

EXAMPLE: Numbers rolled: 2, 9 and 7

$2(x + y) = 2 \times 16 = 32$

VARIATION III: Same as IV, but roll two different coloured regular dice and let one be the multiplier for x and one be the multiplier for y; ten-sided (0-9) die is x; and twelve-sided (1-12) die is y.

EXAMPLE: Numbers rolled: Black 2, white 4, ten-sided (0-9) die is an 8, twelve-sided (1-12) die is a 12

Problem: $2(8) + 4(12) = 16 + 48 = 64$

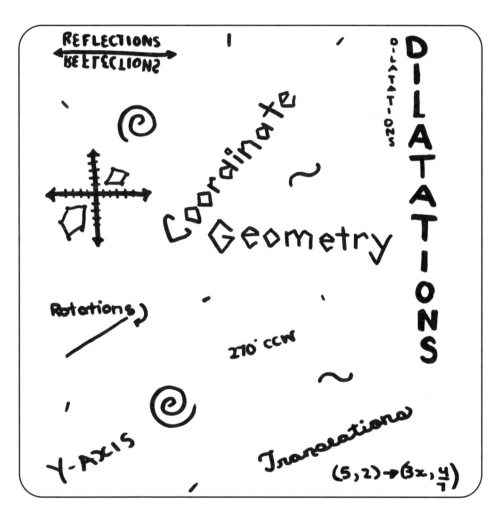

Coordinate
Geometry

MILLIMETRE MAZE

(submitted by Marie Sternberg - class of 2000 Grade 5, England)

LEVEL: Grade 6 - 9

SKILLS: Using a metric ruler, understanding millimetres, concept of horizontal and vertical, right angles, logical reasoning

PLAYERS: 2

EQUIPMENT: One gameboard per player (see reproducibles), one decadie, pencil, ruler

GETTING STARTED: The object of the game is to get from the top left-hand corner to the bottom right-hand corner by using only straight lines, each line being at a right angle to a previous line and staying within the grid. Player One rolls the decadie, and draws a line the corresponding length in millimetres on the grid starting in the top left. At the end of each line drawn, players pencil a little 'node'. Player Two rolls, and draws a line on their grid, with a node at the end. For subsequent rolls, the line can be drawn from any node players have managed to get on their grids, but it must be at a right angle to an existing line and it must run vertically or horizontally. The player who gets to the bottom right-hand corner first, wins. Players must reach the finish with the exact roll, therefore the best strategy is to set up as many nodes as possible to provide several different routes.

VARIATIONS:
1. Play on a larger gameboard whereby using cm squared paper is essential.

2. Players could alternate turns by sharing one larger grid to race to the finish, using different coloured pencils, and using the same set of lines.

THOUGHT PROVOKERS:
1. Is it better to roll high or low rolls throughout the game or does it make a difference?

2. After playing several rounds did you find you were more successful by having multiple nodes that offered alternate routes (i.e. more options)?

The following diagram illustrates only Player One's rolls:

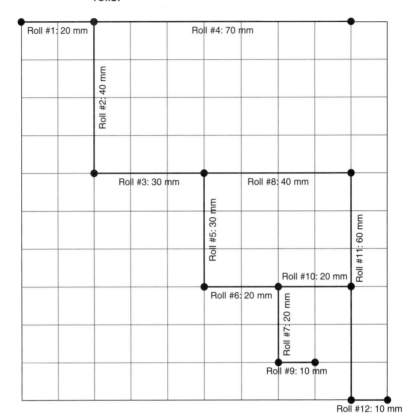

GET TO YOUR CORNER!

LEVEL: Grade 9 - 10

SKILLS: Plotting points on the Cartesian Plane, problem solving

PLAYERS: 2 or 3

EQUIPMENT: Cards Ace - 10 (Ace = 1), one cartesian plane, (see reproducibles), pencil

GETTING STARTED: To begin, players draw a square on the coordinate axis using endpoints: **(8, 8), (-8, 8), (-8, -8)** and **(8, -8)**. The goal of the game is to create a path from the origin **(0, 0)** to any one of the corners. The path is made up of adjacent points. Players take turns drawing two cards at a time and then choosing which point to plot.

EXAMPLE I: **Player One** draws **4, 1**. This could be used as

         (4, 1)   **(1, 4)**

         (-4, 1)   **(-1, 4)**

         (-4, -1)   **(-1, -4)**

         (4, -1)   **(1, -4)**

Player One can choose any one of these eight choices and plots the point. As long as two points are only two units away from each other they may be joined by a line and be used as part of the path (diagonal is acceptable). The first player to reach one of the corners wins.

EXAMPLE II: **Player One:** (8,2) (4,6) (7,3) (5,4) (5,1) (8,0) (5,5) (7,5) (2,0) (6,3) (1,2) (0,4) (0,8) (0,5) (3,7) (1,3) (2,2) (5,8) (2,5) (3,8)

         Player Two: (-7,5) (-5,5) (-2,4) (-4,9) (-2,8) (-3,8) (-7,4) (-8,8) (0,9) (-8,6) (-8,3) (-2,9) (-4,0) (-3,5) (-8,1) (-6,5) (-7,7) (-5,7) (-2,9)

Player One   **Player Two**

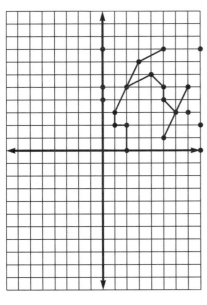 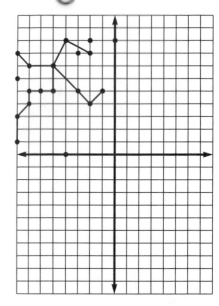

VARIATION: Make the square larger or change the shape of the
                          polygon to make the game more difficult.

√‾‾‾‾‾‾‾‾‾‾‾‾‾
RADICAL RULES: You can name any point on a coordinate plane with two
                          numbers called coordinates. The first number is the x-
                          coordinate (abscissa) and the second number is the y-
                          coordinate (ordinate). The pair is always named in
                          order (first x and then y), thus called an ordered pair.

PLOTTING ALONG

LEVEL: Grade 9 - 10

SKILLS: Ordered pair recognition, plotting points, line recognition

PLAYERS: 2 to 4

EQUIPMENT: Two ten-sided (0-9) dice, bingo chips (different colour for each player), gameboard (see reproducibles)

GETTING STARTED: The goal of the game is to be the first player to have three bingo chips in a straight line. Players roll a die to determine who will begin. Player One rolls the dice and chooses which ordered pair to plot on the gameboard. Player may use any number rolled as either a positive or negative value. Each player does the same until one player has three bingo chips of the same colour in a straight line. If a player puts a chip where there is already a bingo chip, that player may remove the chip and place their own bingo chip in its place. This chip is considered "captured" by the player and counted as 1 point earned. Play continues for a set period of time. **BONUS POINTS** can be earned for correctly calculating the slope of the winning line.

       NOTE: If the cartesian plane used is not large enough for bingo chips, the players may use pencils and use a unique symbol identifying their points e.g. ✱ or ▲).

EXAMPLE:

Player One

□

Player Two

○

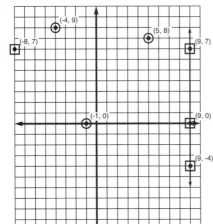

Player One rolls 9, 7   (9, 7)
Player Two rolls 5, 8   (5, 8)
Player One rolls 9, 0   (9, 0)
Player Two rolls 9, 4   (-4, 9)
Player One rolls 8, 7   (-8, 7)
Player Two rolls 0, 1   (-1, 0)
Player One rolls 9, 4   (9, -4)

Player One scores 1 point for creating a vertical line that runs through the points (9, 7) (9, 0) (9, -4).

Probability

PONDERING PROBABILITY

The games in this section are ideal for exploring probability concepts. The games can engage students in a cycle of:

1. Collecting and representing data.

2. Summarizing, comparing and interpreting data.

3. Data analysis including:

- formulating questions.

- deciding whether the data gives them enough information to answer questions.

- describing events as:

- likely/unlikely

- probable/improbable

- certain, impossible, equally likely

- developing and evaluating inferences and predictions for future events based on data.

4. Conducting probability experiments using games to:

- investigate the likelihood of events.

- learn how to quantify the likelihood of events.

- predict the frequency of outcomes and develop outcome charts.

- explain results.

#3 and #4 often go hand in hand. As students reflect on the game and the generated data they usually discover the best way to organize and display data in a meaningful format.

PROBABILITY GAME

The Games Cycle Lets You Explore Probability in a Meaningful Context.

- Evaluate
- New Prediction ❺

❶ Predict

❷ Play
- Formulate Strategies
- Gather Data

❸
- Organize Results
- Display

❹
- Discuss
- Summarize
- Reflect
- Interpret Data

SIXTY SOMETHING

LEVEL: Grade 7 - 9

SKILLS: Order of operations, probability

PLAYERS: 2 to 4

EQUIPMENT: Two thirty-sided (1-30) dice, paper and pencil

GETTING STARTED: Player One rolls the dice and may choose to add, subtract, multiply or divide the numbers rolled. The goal is to reach the total of 60 in three rolls. A player may choose to 'freeze' after the first or second roll, record their number and their play is over. Players continue to take turns and the player closest to 60 for each round earns 1 point. If a player reaches 60 exactly, they earn 2 extra bonus points. The first player to score 20 points is the winner.

EXAMPLE:

Player One:

First Roll: **4**   and   **6**

Player One chooses to multiply the numbers for a total of 24 (4 x 6).

Second Roll: **28**   and   **2**

Player One chooses to add the numbers for a total of 30 (28 + 2). Player One now adds the first and second rolls to equal 54 (30 + 24).

Player One says 'freeze' with 54 and chooses not to take a third roll.

Player Two:

First Roll: **17**   and   **21**

Player Two chooses to add the numbers for a total of 38 (17 + 21).

Second Roll: **25**   and   **5**

Player Two chooses to divide the numbers for a total of 5. Player Two now adds the previous total of 38 to 5 for a total of 43 (38 + 5).

Third Roll:  and

Player Two chooses to multiply the numbers for a total of 17 (17 x 1). Player Two now adds the previous total of 43 to 17 for a perfect total of 60 (43 + 17). Player Two earns 1 point for that round plus 2 extra bonus points for reaching 60 exactly.

Sixty Something

60 60 60 60 60 60 60 60 60 60 60 60 60 60 60 60 60 60 60 60 60 60 60

MACK

the goal of the game is to get closer to Sixty than your partner in 3 rolls. In my last game I was able to get exactly 60 on my second roll.

This is what happened....

On my first roll I rolled an 11 and a 5. I multiplied them and got 55. On my second roll I rolled a 13 and an eight. I subtracted 8 from 13 which equals 5. I added 5 and 55 and got sixty!

139

MYSTERY ROLL

LEVEL: Grade 7 - 12

SKILLS: Sequencing numbers, probability, problem solving - using logical reasoning, making predictions, percent

PLAYERS: 3

EQUIPMENT: One thirty-sided (1-30) die per player, paper, pencil

GETTING STARTED: Each player folds a piece of paper as follows, and records: **G**reatest, **B**etween, **L**east on it.

This paper will serve to hide a player's roll from their opponents. As well, players will place their die, each round, on top of the letter that matches their prediction.

The goal of the game is to have a correct prediction. Players score 1 point for each correct prediction.

Teaching Tip: Teach the game to one small group at a time. Before explaining the rules, roll all three dice in front of the players. Have them identify the **G**reatest roll, **L**east roll and the roll that falls **B**etween. Do this five to ten times - provide enough practice to ensure they understand this concept before proceeding with the game. Example (three rolls):

	Greatest	**B**etween	**L**east
Round One	28	19	6
Round Two	21	7	2
Round Three	15	13	3
Round Four	26	15	5

Step One - Rolling the Die:

To begin each round each player rolls their die behind their paper. They must look at their number and decide whether it is most probably the **G**reatest, **B**etween, or **L**east of the three hidden rolls. Once a player decides on their prediction they place their die on top of the matching letter **G**, **B**, or **L**.

140

Step Two - Predictions:

NOTE: As players gain experience with this game their predictions will become more accurate. A growing understanding of probability (i.e. the odds of rolling any one number and what are most probably Greatest, Least and Between rolls) will only come with practice.

First predictions: In sequence, each player states their prediction to the others. Important information can be gathered by players at this point and used for the second round of predictions.

Second Predictions: This is the last round for players to make predictions. Based on information from the first round, they may either stay with their original first round prediction or change it. Again in sequence, each player states one of the following:

i) I'm staying with **G**, **L** or **B** (their first round prediction)

OR

ii) I'm changing my prediction to **G**, **L** or **B**.

During this second round players must use logical reasoning and their understanding of probability to determine the best prediction for their own hidden roll.

Step Three - Revealing the Rolls:

Once the second round of predictions are completed, players reveal their hidden rolls. Greatest, Between, and Least rolls are determined. Players compare their predictions to the actual ranking of their own roll. Players score a point if their prediction is correct.

EXAMPLE:

Rounds with Predictions:

	Player One	Player Two	Player Three
Roll	26	12	4
Round One Prediction	G	B	L
Round Two Prediction	G	B	L

All players were accurate and score 1 point each.

	Player One	Player Two	Player Three
Roll	8	11	2
Round One Prediction	**B**	**B**	**L**
Round Two Prediction	**L**	**B**	**L**

Only Player Three scores 1 point. Player Two's 11 is **G** and Player One's 8 is **B**.

	Player One	Player Two	Player Three
Roll	28	28	10
Round One Prediction	**G**	**G**	**B**
Round Two Prediction	**G**	**G**	**L**

In this round Players One and Two are both equally **G**reatest Rolls. All three players score 1 point.

	Player One	Player Two	Player Three
Roll	17	26	17
Round One Prediction	**B**	**G**	**B**
Round Two Prediction	**B**	**G**	**L**

In this round 17 is equally **L**east. Only Players Two and Three score a point.

NOTE: PLAYERS SHOULD ROTATE TURNS BEING THE FIRST TO PREDICT EACH NEW ROUND.

THOUGHT PROVOKERS:

You will need to play either 50 or 100 rounds. Every round record <u>G</u>reatest, <u>B</u>etween and <u>L</u>east. Figure out the range between greatest and least. Highlight any interesting rounds using a highlighter (e.g. tie rolls, sequences, unusual winning rolls, 6 = the greatest of the three numbers rolled).

Once you have completed the rounds, answer the following:

1. What is the average range of the rolls?

2. What percentage of the time does a tie roll happen?

3. What percentage of the time did you score a point? If you kept track of all winners, what percentage of the time did all three players score a point?

4. Describe your most unusual round. Try to interpret the probability of that event happening.

5. Write one question for the rest of the group to use with their data.

Mystery Roll

Round	G	B	L	Range	Analyze
13	24	19	17	7	
14	20	14	8		
15	26	21	5	14	
16	29	12	5	24	
17	14	8	3	11	small
18	17	16	6	11	staruck
19	17	10	5	12	
20	12	2	13	11	small sequence
21	27	20	13	14	
22	9	6	1	8	
23	17	9	1	18	
24	28	15	10	18	all scramble
25	29/63		10		tie
26	28	23	9	19	
27	23	20	6	3	
28	13	10	4	9	small sequ.
29	10	8	7	3	
30	25	9	6	19	
31	26	14	8	20	
32	30		7	23	Tie
33	21	6	1	20	
34	30	5	2	28	
35	19	18	11	8	Small sequ
36	23	26	15	14	
37	30	29	15	15	Small sequ.
38	25	8	8	18	
39	20	16	5	15	
40	29	7	4	25	
41	23	21	18	5	
42	12	9	6	6	
43	25	4	19	6	
44	22	16	15	7	
45	23	15	2	27	

143

1. 144, (no) ✓

2. 4/100, 4% of the time ties happened.

3. $\frac{19}{50} = \frac{38}{100}$, 38% of the time I scored.
   $\frac{6}{50} = \frac{12}{100}$, 12% of the time everyone scored.

4. #3 because the highest was 27, the other were both 7. The lowest was directly in the highest, there was a tie, and everyone scored!

5. How many times was the range under 10?
   ✓ Answer: 14 times out of 50, 4/50, 8/100, or 8%.

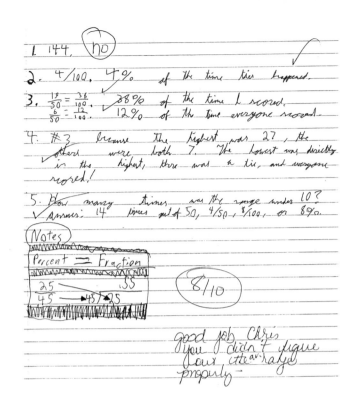

Notes

Percent = Fraction

25 → .55
45 → 45 → .25

8/10

good job Chris
you didn't figure
your average
properly-

MYSTERY ROLL CHALLENGERS

NOTE: READ MYSTERY ROLL PAGE 140 TO UNDERSTAND BASIC RULES

LEVEL: Grade 7 - 12

SKILLS: addition of two-digit numbers with regrouping, or multiplication of two-digit factors, or place value to thousands

PLAYERS: 3 to 5

EQUIPMENT: Two thirty-sided (1-30) dice per player

GETTING STARTED:

I) Addition with Regrouping - Grade 3 and up

Players each roll two dice, find the sum, then make their predictions. Sums would include the range from 2 to 60.

II) Multiplication - Grade 4 and up

Players each roll two dice, find the product, then make their predictions. Products would include the range from 1 to 900.

III) Place Value - Grade 3 and up

Players each roll two dice and make a number (e.g. roll 24, 16 - can make 2 416 or 1 624). Players must form their number before Step 2: Prediction. Numbers ranging from 11 to 3 030.

Single-digit rolls must be used as such, no zeroes allowed (e.g. 6, 24 - can only be 624 or 246 not 6 024 or 2 406).

IV) Playing with Four Players

Increase the difficulty by refining the Prediction Choices to:

EXAMPLE:

Greatest	Greatest Between	Least Between	Least
28	21	17	6

V) Playing with Five Players

Increase the difficulty by refining the Prediction Choices to a 5 scale ranking:

5	4	3	2	1
Greatest Roll	$\longrightarrow$			Least Roll
29	26	17	12	3

INTEGER MYSTERY ROLL

(submitted by Linda Williams)

LEVEL: Grade 7 - 12

SKILLS: Sequencing integers and whole numbers, probability, logical reasoning, predicting

PLAYERS: 3

EQUIPMENT: One thirty-sided (1-30) die per player, paper, pencil

GETTING STARTED: See basic Mystery Rolls Rules page {140}. Once the basic game is understood, change the rules as follows:

1. All odd numbers from 1 - 29 are negative values.

2. All even numbers from 2 - 30 are positive values.

This gives players a range for predicting from -29 to +30.

The game plays out and scores as per regular Mystery Roll rules.

EXAMPLE:

Player One	Player Two	Player Three
-17 predicted	+20 predicted	-3 predicted
Ⓛ	Ⓖ	Ⓑ

All three players were correct in their predictions and all earn 1 point (indicated by circle).

Play continues for a set period of time. The player with the most points is the winner.

ROLLER COASTER

(submitted by Cheri Eck)

LEVEL: Grade 6 - 9

SKILLS: Probability, adding and subtracting with regrouping, integers, mental estimation

PLAYERS: Small group or teacher vs. whole class

EQUIPMENT: One thirty-sided (1-30) die, one gameboard per player (see reproducibles), pencil

GETTING STARTED: The goal of the game is to get as close to zero as possible without ending up in a negative value. A roller is selected for the group. They will roll twelve times for the round. Play begins with the first roll. All players must decide if they wish to select or reject this number for their gameboard. Players must make this decision at the time of the roll. Once players decide what to do with the roll, they fill this number in a plus, minus or reject space in their gameboard.

The roller continues until all twelve rolls have been completed. Any player, once completed their "accept" column, stops play, and waits until all other players have completed their game.

Once all players have completed their boards, they compare answers. The player closest to zero, without going into a negative value is the winner, scores 5 points and is the roller for the next round. The player with the most points after a set period of time is the winner.

EXAMPLE:

Numbers rolled in sequence:

27, 8, 18, 26, 13, 2, 8, 19, 14, 16, 7, 4

Player One

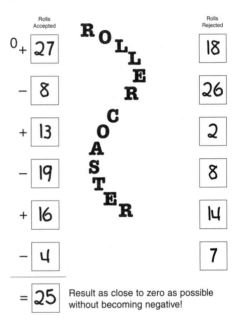

Result as close to zero as possible without becoming negative!

Player Two

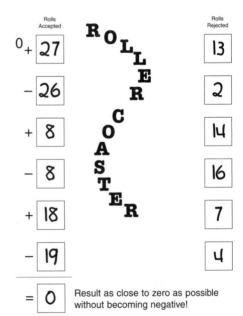

Result as close to zero as possible without becoming negative!

100 WIPE OUT

LEVEL: Grade 6 - 9

SKILLS: Probability, mental estimation, subtraction

PLAYERS: Small groups or whole class, 1 Roller per group

EQUIPMENT: One thirty-sided (1-30) die, one gameboard per player (see reproducibles), pencil

GETTING STARTED: The goal of the game is to subtract numbers from 100 to get as close to zero as possible. One player is selected to roll the die ten times for the round. Play begins with the first roll. All players must decide if they wish to select or reject this number for their gameboard. Players must make this decision at the time of the roll. Once players decide what to do with the roll they fill this number in the appropriate space in their gameboard.

EXAMPLE:

NUMBERS ROLLED IN SEQUENCE:

19, 12, 20, 23, 16, 29, 15, 2, 21, 18

	Rolls Accepted	Rolls Rejected
100 -	19	12
=	81	
-	20	16
=	61	
-	23	15
=	38	
-	29	21
=	9	
-	2	18
=	7	

Players can not go under 0 or they strike out!

The roller continues until all ten rolls are complete. All ten spaces on the gameboard must be filled in. Players subtract their numbers. The player with the difference closest to zero, without going under, wins and becomes the roller for the next round.

THROWING FOR THREE HUNDRED

LEVEL:	Grade 7 - 9
SKILLS:	Multiplication with decimals, addition with regrouping, probability
PLAYERS:	2
EQUIPMENT:	One decadie, one ten-sided (0-9) die per player
GETTING STARTED:	Player One begins by rolling their dice. Players multiply as follows:

 X .

The ten-sided (0-9) die is the decimal value.

40 x .3 = 12

Player One must now decide whether to roll again hoping to roll a product greater than their first roll, or freeze and record this number on their paper. If Player One rolls again and is successful in rolling a new product that is greater than their previous roll (not equal to) then that number is added to their previous product, for an accumulated total. If Player One would like to freeze their accumulated total, they can do so, or that player could choose to roll again.

If the new product rolled is not greater than the previous product rolled, Player One loses all their accumulated points for **that turn**.

Players alternate rolling and accumulating their totals until one player reaches and/or exceeds 300.

Player One's Rolls Only:

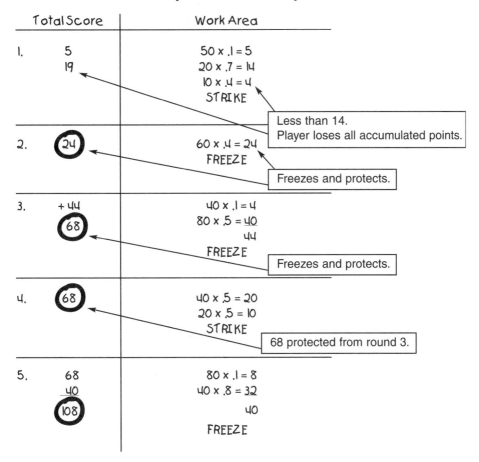

Total Score	Work Area
1. 5 19	50 x .1 = 5 20 x .7 = 14 10 x .4 = 4 STRIKE
	Less than 14. Player loses all accumulated points.
2. (24)	60 x .4 = 24 FREEZE
	Freezes and protects.
3. + 44 (68)	40 x .1 = 4 80 x .5 = 40 44 FREEZE
	Freezes and protects.
4. (68)	40 x .5 = 20 20 x .5 = 10 STRIKE
	68 protected from round 3.
5. 68 40 (108)	80 x .1 = 8 40 x .8 = 32 40 FREEZE

The first player to reach 300 first in even turns is the winner.

1. When is it a good decision to freeze and keep your accumulated points without taking another roll?

2. Are certain numbers safer to roll after? Explain.

3. Which combinations of numbers give a player the best products?

4. What is the greatest possible, least possible and average product a player can roll?

ATTACKING THE M AND M'S!

LEVEL: Grade 8 and up

SKILLS: Calculating mean, median and mode, analyzing data, estimating, mental math

PLAYERS: 2 - 4 of equal skill level

EQUIPMENT: One twenty-sided (1-20) die per player, calculator (optional), paper, pencil

GETTING STARTED: Players attempt to target the mean in round one, the median in round two and lastly the mode in round three during three consecutive rounds of play.

For round one, all players will be estimating and calculating the mean of their own numbers rolled. The goal of this round is to create a list of numbers (each player creates their own data) that has a mean (the average of all one player's numbers) that is closest to or equal to the target number.

The twenty-sided (1-20) die is rolled to set the target number for all players to use during this round. Each player now alternates rolling their own twenty-sided (1-20) die and continues to calculate the average of these numbers. All players must have at least three numbers (i.e. values) in their list before they can freeze. After one player verbalizes "freeze" all other players have the option to roll their last number for their list. The player with the closest mean to the target earns 1 point.

EXAMPLE: Target Rolled: 8

Player rolls: 8, 19, 4, 3, 1 (freezes)

Mean = sum of the values ÷ number of values
= 35 ÷ 5 = 7

7 is the mean. Player One is only 1 away from the target number. Players compare their means after equal turns. The player closest to the mean earns 1 point.

On round two, players play in a similar manner, but they are now creating a list of values that result in calculating the median (middle value) which is closest to the target number rolled at the beginning of the game. Remember, all players use the same number rolled as their target number.

EXAMPLE:
Target Rolled: 12

Player One's List: 1, 4, 6, (12) 13, 17, 20

Player One verbalizes "freeze".

Player Two's List: 1, 7, 9, (15) 16, 18, 18

Since Player One's median is exact to the target, Player One earns the point for this round.

During the third round of play, players are attempting to target the mode of the rolled numbers. The mode is the value that occurs most often in a set of data.

The twenty-sided (1-20) die is rolled to set the target.

EXAMPLE:
Target roll = 7

Players now alternate rolling their own twenty-sided (1-20) die creating a set of numbers that would have 7 as a possible mode. The player closest to, earns the point.

EXAMPLE:

	1	3	8		17	
Player One:	1 2 3		7 8 9		15 17 18	

		4	7			
		2 4	7			
Player Two:	2	4 5 6 7	9 10			19

Player One verbalizes "freeze" but since Player Two has rolled three 7's and Player One has rolled only one 7, Player Two would earn the point.

153

IT'S PROBABLY MR. WOLF

NOTE: This activity grew out of one of our simplest primary games. The probability extensions are excellent for Grades 6 - 9.

LEVEL: Grade 6 - 9

SKILLS: Conduct a probability experiment, analyze and interpret data, predicting, average

PLAYERS: Cooperative pairs, contributing to whole class data

EQUIPMENT: Each pair: Cards Ace - Queen (Ace = 1, Jack = 11, Queen = 12), two regular dice, paper, pencil, class chart

GETTING STARTED: There are four levels to this activity.

Level I: addition only

Level II: addition and subtraction only

Level III: addition, subtraction and multiplication only

Level IV: addition, subtraction, multiplication and division

Players arrange their cards into a clock as follows:

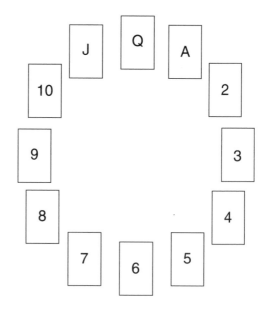

When level one begins, players roll the two dice, add them and turn over the corresponding number on the clock. PLAYERS MUST TALLY ALL ROLLS TAKEN as the question to answer is: How many rolls to turn over all cards, using addition only (Q = 12) - 2 (1 cannot be rolled for the adding only Level 1 play). Players continue rolling, tallying and turning over their cards when possible. If a number is rolled a second time, and the card is already turned over, players must still tally that as a roll.

AFTER EACH LEVEL OF PLAY

When all cards are turned over players do the following:

1. Total their tally and record this on the class chart.

2. In their math book, record this number and which numbers were the most difficult to roll and the easiest to roll.

3. Record a prediction for the next level II where both addition and subtraction can be used for total number of rolls, most difficult numbers to get, easiest numbers to get.

LEVEL II

Play as above but when the dice are rolled players may do as follows:

Roll: 6, 2	$6 + 2 = 8$	turn over the 8
	$6 - 2 = 4$	turn over the 4
	1 TALLY	
Roll: 6, 5	$6 + 5 = 11$	turn over the 11
	$6 - 5 = 1$	turn over the 1
	1 TALLY	

All the numbers Q - Ace can be turned over (i.e. 12 - 1). Once the level is complete, return to AFTER EACH LEVEL OF PLAY and complete the questions.

LEVEL III

Play as above but when the dice are rolled players may do the following:

Roll: 4, 2	$4 + 2 = 6$	turn over the 6
	$4 - 2 = 2$	turn over the 2
	$4 \times 2 = 8$	turn over the 8
	1 TALLY	

Go to AFTER EACH LEVEL OF PLAY and complete the questions.

LEVEL IV

Play as above but when the dice are rolled players may do the following:

Roll: 6, 2   6 + 2 = 8   turn over the 8
               6 − 2 = 4   turn over the 4
               6 x 2 = 12   turn over the 12
               6 ÷ 2 = 3   turn over the 3

Are there any other rolls that give a player 4 possible numbers to turn over?

When all four levels have been completed by the class, all groups can now begin to analyze the data.

1. What is the average number of rolls to turn over all cards in each of the 4 levels? At what level is the most significant change in the average found? Explain why you think it happens at that level.

156

GRAPHING OPERATIONS

LEVEL: Grade 6 - 10

SKILLS: Gathering, organizing and interpreting data, +, −, x, ÷

PLAYERS: Students can work in groups of two or three

EQUIPMENT: Two ten-sided (0-9) dice, gameboard (see reproducibles), paper, pencil

ACTIVITY: Players will be rolling the dice a total of twenty times and recording the sums on the gameboard.

EXAMPLE: **VARIATION I**

	0	1	2	3	4	5	6	7	8	9	10	11	12	13	14	15	16	17	18	19	20
7					5 - 1																
6					4 + 0																
5				5 - 2	4 - 0		6 - 0					6 + 5									
4				7 - 4	4 + 0		6 + 0	9 - 2				9 + 2									
3		6 - 5		6 - 3	4 - 0		5 + 1	5 + 2				9 + 2									
2		7 - 6		3 - 0	7 - 3	9 - 4	4 + 2	7 + 0	4 + 4			8 + 3		4 + 9							
1	4 - 4	6 - 5	4 - 2	3 + 0	9 - 5	8 - 3	7 - 1	9 - 2	7 + 1	6 + 3	7 + 3	5 + 6		7 + 6	9 + 5						

This represents rolling two ten-sided (0-9) dice twenty times and recording the sum and the difference.

THOUGHT PROVOKERS:

1. Which sum is most likely to be rolled most often?

2. What is the most common shape for the histogram? Why?

3. Which sum is least likely to be rolled?

4. (Challenger) What is the experimental probability for each possible sum?

VARIATION I: Record the difference in the two numbers rolled. Also multiplication and division can be included.

VARIATION II: Change the number of rolls possible (30, 40) and see how it effects the histogram.

VARIATION III: Each player has their own gameboard (see reproducibles). Players alternate rolling one twenty-sided (1-20) die and filling in their graph until they reach the top of one column. Players calculate the mean, median and mode of their data. Players compare their findings with each other.

BIG SUMS

LEVEL: Grade 6 - 10

SKILLS: Problem solving, gathering data, recording data, interpreting data

PLAYERS: Students work in groups of two, three or four

EQUIPMENT: Thirty-six regular dice per group, chart (see reproducibles), paper, pencil,

ACTIVITY I: The goal of the activity is to find the sum of thirty-six dice after they have been rolled.

TEACHING TIP: Allow students several rounds to develop their own method of adding the dice. Use Chart I to record the methods (see student samples). Teach the patterns below and show the students how to group the dice.

1	2	6
2	4	7
3	6	8
+ 4	+ 8	+ 9
10	20	30

Our Prediction	Sum	+ / - on Prediction
110	Sum = 104	6
104	Sum = 132	28
120	Sum = 123	3

THOUGHT PROVOKERS:

1. What is the most efficient method for using the patterns?

2. In which order should we use the patterns to be most efficient? Why?

3. What is the largest sum possible? What is the smallest sum we could have?

ACTIVITY II: The goal is the same but we are trying to determine the range of possible sums. Use Chart II to record the sums that are used.

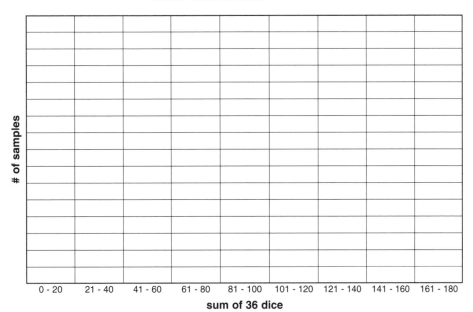

sum of 36 dice

THOUGHT PROVOKERS:

1. What is your estimate for the mean value of the sums?

2. Can anyone give an explanation for the mean?

3. (Challenger) What is the mean sum of 48 dice?

159

SEEMINGLY SIMPLE DOUBLES

LEVEL: Grade 6 - 10

SKILLS: Data collection, organization and interpretation of data, probability

PLAYERS: Students work in groups of two or three

EQUIPMENT: Thirty-six regular dice, paper and pencil, pencil crayons (optional)

ACTIVITY: Students are required to arrange the dice in pairs and group them in blocks resembling a histogram.

EXAMPLE: **After a roll:**

TEACHING TIP: Do this activity over a long period and post the histograms. You may begin to see some interesting patterns.

THOUGHT PROVOKERS:

1. What is the maximum number of pairs possible? Why?

2. What is the average number of pairs?

3. What is the minimum number of pairs possible? Why?

4. What shape (or type of distribution) is most common for the histograms?

VARIATION I: Group only pairs of the same colour together. Answer the same **THOUGHT PROVOKERS**.

VARIATION II: Group triples. Answer the same **THOUGHT PROVOKERS**.

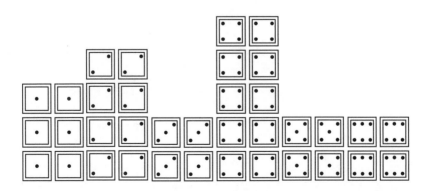

SNAPPY AVERAGES

LEVEL: Grade 7 and up

SKILLS: Adding positive and negative integers and calculating the average

PLAYERS: 2 of equal skill level

EQUIPMENT: Cards Ace - King (Ace = 1, Jack = 11, Queen = 12, King = 0), one ten-sided (0-9) die, paper, pencil, calculator (optional)

GETTING STARTED: To begin, one player rolls the ten-sided (0-9) die to determine the number of shared cards players will be dealt. Red cards will have a negative value and black will be positive. At the same time, both players now calculate (mentally or paper/pencil computation) the average sum of all the number values shown on the cards.

EXAMPLE: Die rolled = 6

Six cards are flipped up for both players to use.

3	6	2	8	1	3
B	B	R	R	B	R

$3 + 6 - 2 - 8 + 1 - 3 = -3$

Average = $-3 \div 6 = -.5$

The first player to correctly verbalize the answer "negative .5" or "negative one-half" earns 1 point.

Play continues for a set period of time. The player with the most points wins.

√RADICAL RULES: An average is a number that summarizes a set of data by giving some sense of the typical value. To find the average of several quantities, divide their sum by the number of quantities. The mean is a type of average.

$$\text{Mean} = \frac{\text{sum of the values}}{\text{number of values}}$$

Fractions and Ratios

ADDING FRACTION WAR

LEVEL: Grade 6 - 9

SKILLS: Adding proper fractions with unlike denominators, estimating, calculating decimal equivalents

PLAYERS: 2 or 4: 2 vs. 2

EQUIPMENT: Cards Ace - King (Ace = 1, Jack = 11, Queen = 12, King = 0), paper, pencil, calculator

GETTING STARTED: Players divide cards evenly between themselves. Players turn over four cards each, making two proper fractions and adding them. The player with the greatest sum collects the cards. In the event of a tie both players take their own cards and places them into their point pile.

Players must verbalize their sum in the simplest form.

EXAMPLE: **Player One** $\dfrac{6}{12} + \dfrac{8}{9} = \dfrac{1}{2} + \dfrac{8}{9} = \dfrac{9}{18} + \dfrac{16}{18} = \dfrac{25}{18} = 1\dfrac{7}{18}$

Calculator Check: 1.38

Player Two $\dfrac{9}{12} + \dfrac{5}{7} = \dfrac{3}{4} + \dfrac{5}{7} = \dfrac{21}{28} + \dfrac{20}{28} = \dfrac{41}{28} = 1\dfrac{13}{28}$

Calculator Check: 1.46

Player Two takes all four cards.

Play continues for a set period of time. The player with the most cards wins.

VARIATION: Have players estimate which sum is the greatest before doing calculations. Use a calculator to convert fractions to decimals to check.

TEACHING TIP: Have players visualize their fractions to one whole

THINK: $\dfrac{6}{12}$ is one-half + $\dfrac{8}{9}$ is <u>almost</u> one whole

Therefore my answer should be about $1\dfrac{1}{2}$.

ANY WHOLE NUMBER

LEVEL: Grade 6 - 9

SKILLS: Rounding and estimating proper fractions, adding fractions, adding fractions to the nearest whole

PLAYERS: 2

EQUIPMENT: Cards Ace - 9 (Ace = 1)

GETTING STARTED: Each player takes six cards and arranges them into three proper fractions. The goal is to round and estimate your fractions to be as close to any whole number as possible. Exact answers are not necessary.

EXAMPLE:

Player One: | 4 | 7 | 3 | 2 | 1 | 2 |

Player arranges them as follows:

$$\frac{2}{2} + \frac{3}{4} + \frac{1}{7}$$

Think 1 + 3/4 and almost 1/8 close to 2 wholes.

Player Two: | 5 | 1 | 8 | 6 | 4 | 5 |

Player arranges them as follows:

$$\frac{6}{8} + \frac{1}{4} + \frac{5}{5}$$

Think 6/8 = 3/4, therefore 3/4 + 1/4 + 5/5 = 2 exact.

Player Two collects all of the cards for closest to (in fact exact) to the wholes.

FRACTION SUBTRACTION WAR

LEVEL: Grade 6 - 9

SKILLS: Subtracting proper fractions with unlike denominators, estimating, using a calculator

PLAYERS: 2 or 4: 2 vs. 2

EQUIPMENT: Cards Ace - Queen (Ace = 1, Jack = 11, Queen = 12), paper, pencil, calculator

GETTING STARTED: Each player takes four cards. Players now arrange their cards to make two proper fractions that when subtracted create the least possible fraction. NO NEGATIVE VALUES ALLOWED.

EXAMPLE: **Player One:** | 9 | 3 | 11 | 5 |

Possible arrangements include:

$$1. \frac{9}{11} - \frac{3}{5} \qquad 2. \frac{5}{11} - \frac{3}{9} \qquad 3. \frac{5}{9} - \frac{3}{11}$$

Player One decides to calculate:

$$2. \frac{5}{11} - \frac{3}{9} = \frac{45}{99} - \frac{33}{99} = \frac{12}{99} \text{ or } .12 \text{ (calculator check)}$$

Player One now compares their answer to Player Two's. The player with the least fraction takes all the cards and places them into their point pile.

In the event of a tie, both players take their own cards and places them into their point pile.

Players must verbalize their answer in its simplest form (i.e. fraction or decimal).

Play continues for a set period of time. The player with the most cards is the winner.

NOTE: To simplify game use cards 1, 2, 3, 4, 6, 8, 12 only. These are what students find as more "Friendly Fraction Numbers".

TARGET ZERO

(submitted by Nancy McGuire)

LEVEL: Grade 6 - 9

SKILLS: Adding and subtracting tenths on a number line, including negative numbers

PLAYERS: 2, or solitaire

EQUIPMENT: One decadie, one number line per player (see reproducibles), pencil, and pointer (paper clip)

GETTING STARTED: Each player labels the blank number line using intervals of 10ths. Both players start at 1 whole number. Player rolls the decadie, uses this as a decimal value, and subtracts or adds to get to zero. The object of the game is to reach zero by an exact roll. Players may add or subtract their roll to do so. The first player to reach zero scores 1 point.

EXAMPLE:

PLAYER ONE'S ROLLS ONLY

First roll:	20	$1 - .2 = .8$
Second roll:	60	$.8 - .6 = .2$
Third roll:	30	$.2 - .3 = -.1$
Fourth roll:	90	$-.1 + .9 = .8$
Fifth roll:	80	$.8 - .8 = 0$

Player scores a point.

VARIATION: Use a decadie and a ten-sided (0-9) die. Add or subtract with hundredths. In this variation, a player scores a point if they get within -.05 to .05.

Roll: 20 and 9	$1 - .29 = .71$
Roll: 30 and 6	$.71 - .36 = .35$
Roll: 40 and 4	$.35 - .44 = -.09$
Roll: 10 and 1	$-.09 + .11 = .02$

Player scores a point.

DOUBLE REDUCE SNAP

LEVEL: Grade 7 - 9

SKILLS: Doubling fractions, reducing fractions to simplest form

PLAYERS: 2 equal skill level

EQUIPMENT: Two twelve-sided (1-12) dice

GETTING STARTED: At the same time each player rolls one of the twelve-sided (1-12) dice. Players mentally build the proper fraction and double it.

EXAMPLE:

$$\frac{5}{7} \text{ doubled} = \frac{10}{7} = 1\frac{3}{7}$$

The first player to verbalize the doubled fraction in its simplest form earns the point.

Some More Examples:

$$\frac{3}{5} \text{ doubled} = \frac{6}{5} = 1\frac{1}{5}$$

$$\frac{1}{9} \text{ doubled} = \frac{2}{9} \text{ Already in its simplest form.}$$

$$\frac{8}{12} \text{ doubled} = \frac{16}{12} = 1\frac{4}{12} = 1\frac{1}{3}$$

This game is excellent for mental math with equivalent fractions.

If both players give a correct answer at the same time, both players earn a point.

VARIATION: To increase difficulty, both players roll two twelve-sided (1-12) dice and build their own proper fraction. Players must analyze both outcomes and verbalize which doubled fraction is the greatest.

EXAMPLE: **Player One**

$$\frac{6}{7} \text{ doubled} = \frac{12}{7} = 1\frac{5}{7}$$

Player Two

$$\frac{4}{5} \text{ doubled} = \frac{8}{5} = 1\frac{3}{5}$$

Player Two verbalizes 1 5/7 is greater than 1 3/5 even though they did not roll the greater fraction.

CONNOR'S EQUIVALENT RACE

LEVEL: Grade 6 - 9

SKILLS: Building equivalent fractions

PLAYERS: 4: 2 vs. 2

EQUIPMENT: Cards Ace - Queen (Ace = 1, Jack = 11, Queen = 12)

GETTING STARTED: The goal of the game is to be the first player to build a pair of equivalent proper fractions. No whole numbers are allowed (e.g. 5/5, 6/6 or 2/2, etc.). Play begins by each player dealing out four cards and building two proper fractions. No identical fractions allowed (e.g. 2/9 = 2/9 or 1/3 = 1/3).

EXAMPLE:

Player One	Player Two
$\dfrac{7}{9} \quad \dfrac{2}{8}$	$\dfrac{3}{6} \quad \dfrac{2}{3}$

Cards are now placed between the players. Players now alternate drawing one card at a time. Player may use this card in their fraction sentence or discard it for the other player to use.

Player One's Moves Only:

1. $\dfrac{7}{9} \quad \dfrac{2}{8}$ Draws 1. Discards.

2. $\dfrac{7}{9} \quad \dfrac{2}{8}$ Draws 10. Exchanges 9 for 10.

3. $\dfrac{7}{10} \quad \dfrac{2}{8}$ Draws 12. Exchanges 12 for 10.

4. $\dfrac{7}{12} \quad \dfrac{2}{8}$ Draws 12. Discards 12.

5. $\dfrac{7}{12} \quad \dfrac{2}{8}$ Draws 4. Exchanges 4 for 2.

6. $\dfrac{7}{12} \quad \dfrac{4}{8}$ Draws 11. Discards.

Thinks 7/12 is close to 1/2. 4/8 is already 1/2. Hoping for a 6 to build 6/12 = 4/8 = 1/2.

7. $\dfrac{7}{12} \quad \dfrac{4}{8}$ Draws 4. Discards.

170

8. $\dfrac{7}{12}$ $\dfrac{4}{8}$ Draws $\boxed{6}$. Exchanges.

$\dfrac{6}{12}$ is equivalent to $\dfrac{4}{8}$ and wins the round.

Remember, players are alternating drawing and discarding throughout the game. Players can choose to pick up the discard or pick up the top card off the deck.

Play continues for a set period of time. The player with the most points is the winner.

BEAT MR. MATHJACK

(Submitted by Nancy McGuire)

LEVEL: Grade 6 and up

SKILLS: Equivalent fractions, adding fractions, probability, mental calculations

PLAYERS: Group of four

EQUIPMENT: Fraction cards, one sheet for each player (see reproducibles), bingo chips or other counters

GETTING STARTED: To make the deck have each player cut up their sheet of cards and write their initials on the back side of the card. Four students will combine their cards making one large deck. At the end of the game they can collect their own cards and keep in a plastic bag for use at another time.

Choose one player to be Mr. Mathjack, the dealer

The goal of the game is to get a hand of cards showing a value that is greater than Mr. Mathjack's hand, but not more than one whole number (12/12).

Mr. Mathjack deals each player two cards face up so that all players can see their value. Mr. Mathjack deals one of their own cards face down so that players only see one of his cards. Players determine the value of their hand. Any player who has a whole number using only two cards, has a MATHJACK and automatically wins two counters. Beginning with the player to Mr. Mathjack's left, Mr. Mathjack asks the player if they want a card. If they are confident with their hand, they say no. If a player wants a card, Mr. Mathjack deals the next card and continues dealing to that player until they say stop or until they go over a whole number. Mr. Mathjack continues on to the next player and repeats the process.

After all players have taken the cards they need, then Mr. Mathjack turns over their card that is face down. Mr. Mathjack determines the value of their hand and makes a decision about taking cards. Mr. Mathjack has different rules on taking a card. They must take a card on 9/12, and must stop on 10/12 or more.

If a player has a hand greater than or equal to Mr. Mathjack, he earns one counter. If a player has less than Mr. Mathjack, then the player does not earn a counter. Mr. Mathjack collects the cards, deals again, and continues to deal until the deck has been used up. Switch Mr. Mathjack and continue for a set amount of time.

 **TEACHING TIP:**

For newer players, have players make up a card showing the equivalents of the fractions in 12ths (e.g. 1/6 = 2/12; 1/4 = 3/12; 1/3 = 4/12; 1/2 = 6/12) and keep it on the table for each to look at. After playing for a while players will have these equivalencies memorized.

Before playing or after playing a few times, discuss the make up of the deck. Show the ratio of the individual cards to the deck. Show an overhead of an uncut sheet and discuss that there are 4 sheets in each deck. Players will think about the probability of the cards being drawn.

FRACTION ROLL OFFS

LEVEL: Grade 6 - 9

SKILLS: Multiplying a whole number by a fraction

PLAYERS: 2 or 4: 2 vs. 2

EQUIPMENT: Cards Ace - Queen (Ace = 1, Jack = 11, Queen = 12), one twenty-sided (1-20) die

GETTING STARTED: Each player takes two cards and arranges them into a proper fraction.

EXAMPLE: **Player One:** $\dfrac{3}{5}$ **Player Two:** $\dfrac{7}{9}$

Players now roll a twenty-sided (1-20) die and multiply the proper fraction by the whole number.

Roll: 12

$$12 \times \frac{3}{5} \qquad\qquad 12 \times \frac{7}{9}$$

√‾‾‾‾‾ RADICAL RULES: When you multiply a whole number by a proper fraction, the product is less than the number you started with.

Players compare their answers. The player with the greatest product takes all of their cards and places them into their point pile.

In the event of a tie, both players take their own cards and place them into their point pile. Players must verbalize their answer in its simplest form.

Player One: $\dfrac{12}{1} \times \dfrac{3}{5} = \dfrac{36}{5} = 7\dfrac{1}{5}$

(which is less than what we started with - see Radical Rules)

$\dfrac{3}{5}$ is slightly more than $\dfrac{1}{2}$ $12 \times \dfrac{1}{2} = 6$

Our answer makes sense as 7 1/5 is slightly more than 6.

Player Two: $\dfrac{12}{1} \times \dfrac{7}{9} = \dfrac{4}{1} \times \dfrac{7}{3} = \dfrac{28}{3} = 9\dfrac{1}{3}$

Player Two verbalizes 9 1/3 is greater than 7 1/5 and takes all of the cards.

FRACTION "X"

LEVEL: Grade 6 - 9

SKILLS: Multiplying proper fractions with whole numbers, unlike denominators, estimating, using a calculator

PLAYERS: 2 or 4: 2 vs. 2

EQUIPMENT: Cards Ace - Queen (Ace = 1, Jack = 11, Queen = 12)

GETTING STARTED: Each player takes four cards and arranges them into two proper fractions. Players now arrange their cards to make the largest possible fraction product.

Player One: 1, 5, 3, 10

$$\frac{5}{10} \times \frac{1}{3} = \frac{5}{30} = \frac{1}{6} \qquad \text{OR} \qquad \frac{1}{10} \times \frac{3}{5} = \frac{3}{50} \text{ Way less!}$$

$$\frac{3}{10} \times \frac{1}{5} = \frac{5}{30} = \frac{3}{50} \text{ Way less!}$$

Player chooses first arrangement.

Player One now compares their answer to Player Two's. The player with the greatest product takes all of the cards and places them into their point pile.

In the event of a tie, both players take their own cards and place them into their point pile.

Players must verbalize their answer in its simplest form or decimal.

√‾RADICAL RULES: Have students visualize:

$$\frac{5}{10} \times \frac{1}{3} \text{ is really: } \frac{1}{2} \times \frac{1}{3}; \text{ is really: What is } \frac{1}{3} \text{ of } \frac{1}{2} ?$$

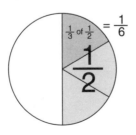

FRACTION GET BACK

(submitted by Nancy McGuire)

LEVEL: Grade 7 - 10

SKILLS: Plotting integers and negative/positive fractions, adding and subtracting, problem solving

PLAYERS: 2

EQUIPMENT: Fraction cards (see reproducibles), gameboard (see reproducibles), bingo chips or markers, operation (+/−) die (or use a regular die 1, 2, 3 = positive values, 4, 5, 6 = negative values)

GETTING STARTED: Players shuffle the deck and place it face down between the two players. The goal of the game is to get back to zero in order to score a point. Each player places their bingo chip or marker at zero. Player One rolls the die to determine if the card turned over will have a negative or positive value. The player then moves their marker the corresponding number of points. A player may add or subtract the number to their position on the number line. Play continues for a set period of time. If the deck is completed before a player reaches zero, it is reshuffled.

EXAMPLE:

Player One	Player Two
Rolls (+), draws 1/4 Moves to +1/4 Records: 0 + 1/4 = 1/4	Rolls (+), draws 1/2 Moves to 1/2 Records: 0 + 1/2 = 1/2
Rolls (−), draws 1/2 Moves to -1/4 Records 1/4 + -1/2 = -1/4	Rolls (−), draws 1/6 Moves to 2/6 Records: 1/2 + -1/6 = 2/6
Rolls (−), draws 3/6 Moves to 1/4 (1/6 = 2/12) Records: -1/4 − -3/6 = 1/4	Rolls (−), draws 1/2 Moves to -1/6 Records: 2/6 + -1/2 = 1/6
Rolls (+), draws 6/12 Moves to -1/4 Records: 1/4 − 6/12 = -1/4	Rolls (−), draws 1/3 Moves to -1/2 Records: -1/6 + -1/3 = -1/2
Rolls (+), draws 1/4 Moves to 0 Records: -1/4 + 1/4 = 0	Rolls (+), draws 1/12 Moves to -5/12 Records: -1/2 + 1/12 = -5/12

Player One scores a point.

FRACTION PRODUCTION

LEVEL: Grade 7 and up

SKILLS: Multiplying proper and improper fractions, reducing fractions, comparing fractions

PLAYERS: 2 to 4 or 2 vs. 2

EQUIPMENT: Cards Ace - 9 (Ace = 1), one twelve-sided (1-12) die, calculator (optional)

GETTING STARTED: The goal of the game is to be the player with the fraction sentence closest to the rolled target. Each player is dealt four cards from which to build their fractions. The die is rolled to set a target that players will attempt to reach by multiplying their two fractions.

EXAMPLE: Player One rolls the die.

Die rolled = 11

Players manipulate their cards to build the following fractions:

Player One: $\dfrac{6}{2} \times \dfrac{9}{3} = 9$

Player Two: $\dfrac{7}{1} \times \dfrac{6}{4} = 10.5$

Since 10.5 is closer to 11 than 9, Player Two earns Player One's cards and places them into their point pile. The player with the most points after a set period of time is the winner.

BRAINY FRACTIONS

LEVEL: Grade 7 and up

SKILLS: Comparing fractions, converting to decimals, adding and subtracting fractions

PLAYERS: 2

EQUIPMENT: Two regular dice, cards Ace - Queen (Ace = 1, Jack = 11, Queen = 12), paper, pencil, calculator

GETTING STARTED: The goal of the game is for players to match their fractions as close to the fractions created with the cards.

Step One

The number indicates how many fractions in simplest form the player is allowed to record on paper before the "card fraction" is created.

EXAMPLE: Player One rolls [dice] .(re-roll [die]).

Player One records any three fractions of their choice:

$$\frac{1}{4}, \frac{3}{7}, \frac{8}{9}$$

Player Two also rolls their die at the same time.

EXAMPLE: Roll: [die]

Player Two now records their fractions.

$$\frac{2}{3}, \frac{5}{8}, \frac{1}{2}, \frac{1}{8}$$

Step Two: Creating the Target Fraction

One player takes the two cards off the top of the deck and makes a proper fraction

e.g. $\frac{3}{8}$

Players now compare their recorded fractions to the card fraction. The player who has the fraction closest to the card fraction takes the cards. If both players are equal to the card fraction then each player takes one of the cards.

$$\frac{3}{7} \text{ is closest for Player One} \qquad \frac{3}{7} = .43 \text{ (.05 away)}$$

$$\frac{1}{2} \text{ is closest for Player Two} \qquad \frac{1}{2} = .50 \text{ (.12 away)}$$

Players may need to use a calculator to determine who is closest to the card target.

$$\frac{3}{8} = .38$$

Player One is closest to the card fraction and takes the cards and places them into their point pile. Each card is equal to 1 point at the end of the game.

Players begin the next round by rolling their regular die, recording new fractions, and setting a "card fraction".

Play continues for a set period of time. The player with the most cards is the winner.

VARIATION:

Play as above. Players however may add or subtract any combination of their recorded fractions to reach the "card fraction".

ROCK 'N RATIOS

LEVEL: Grade 8 and up

SKILLS: Writing ratios using a colon, comparing ratios, expressing ratios as fractions, decimals and percents

PLAYERS: 2 to 4

EQUIPMENT: One thirty-sided (1-30) die per player, paper, pencil, calculators (optional)

GETTING STARTED: The goal of the game is to be the player with their ratio expressed as the highest percent or lowest percent, depending on the roll of the regular die (i.e. 1, 3, 5, lowest percent scores a point; 2, 4, 6, highest percent scores a point).

To begin, each player rolls their thirty-sided (1-30) die three times. Each number is recorded in the order they were rolled. The first number rolled will be the first number in their ratio compared to the sum of all their numbers rolled.

EXAMPLE: Rolls: 5, 18, 11

The number 5 is now being compared to 5 + 18 + 11 = 34 therefore 5:34.

This ratio is already expressed in its simplest form. However, players must now record their ratios as fractions, decimals and finally as a percent.

EXAMPLE: $5:34 = \dfrac{5}{34} = .15 = 15\%$

Therefore 5 is 15% of 34

15% would now be compared to the other player's percent(s). To determine who earns the point, players alternate rolling the regular die (i.e. odd numbers rolled the lowest percent will win, and an even number the highest percent will win).

EXAMPLE: **Player One rolls:** 18, 6, 24

Player Two rolls: 3, 11, 29

Both players now calculate the ratio of their first number rolled to the sum of all three numbers rolled and write this using a colon.

Player One: 18:48

Player Two: 3:43

Players now simplify their ratios, if necessary.

Player One: 3:8

Player Two: 3:43 (both 3 and 43 are prime numbers)

Now players express their ratios as fractions, decimals and percents.

Player One: $\dfrac{3}{8}$ = .38 = 38%

Player Two: $\dfrac{3}{43}$ = .07 = 7%

One player now rolls the regular die to determine the winner.

Player One rolls: 5

Since 5 is odd, the player with the least percent earns the point.

Since 7% is less than 38%, Player Two scores 1 point.

Play continues for a set period of time. The player with the most points is the winner.

Mixed Bag

LEAST COMMON MULTIPLE SNAP

LEVEL: Grade 6 - 9

SKILLS: Finding the least common multiple, prime factorization

PLAYERS: 2 vs. 2, equal skill level

EQUIPMENT: One twelve-sided (1-12) die, paper, pencil

GETTING STARTED: Teams sit across from each other and have a divider hiding their work. The goal of the game is to be the first team to give the least common multiple for a set of three rolled numbers.

Play begins by one team rolling the twelve-sided (1-12) die three times. Both teams record these numbers. Teams now must calculate the LCM for that set of numbers. The first team to give the correct answer out loud scores 3 points.

EXAMPLE: Rolls: 5, 6, 4 (answer = 60)

TEACHING TIP: Help students to work through the following steps to calculate the LCM.

1. Find the prime factorization of each number.

$5 = 5 \times 1$
$6 = 2 \times 3$
$4 = 2 \times 2$

2. Next, find the common factors.

$5 = 5 \times 1$
$6 = \boxed{2} \times 3$
$4 = \boxed{2} \times 2$

3. Next, multiply the common factors and the extra factors.

$2 \times 2 \times 3 \times 5 = 60 \qquad LCM = 60$

common   extra
factor   factors

Three new numbers are rolled for the next round. The first team to identify the LCM correctly scores 3 points. Play continues for a set period of time. The team with the most points is the winner.

MULTIPLES TO THE END

(submitted by Gillian Walston, Gr. 6, Beaumont)

LEVEL: Grade 6 - 9
Variation: Grade 6 - 9

SKILLS: Common multiples, multiplication, factors

PLAYERS: 2 - 4 (teams of 2 vs. 2)

EQUIPMENT: One thirty-sided (1-30) die, one ten-sided (0-9) die, gameboard (see reproducibles), paper, pencil (one decadie - variation)

GETTING STARTED: The goal of the game is to have the greatest number of points after five rounds. Play begins by rolling the ten-sided (0-9) die (re-roll 0). Players record this number for the fact family on their own gameboard.

Players now alternate rolling the thirty-sided (1-30) die and recording this number on their gameboard. If the number is a multiple of the "Fact Family" it is circled and scores at the end of the round. A total of ten rolls are taken by each player, per round.

EXAMPLE:

Round #1 Fact Family 2	18	15	14	19	29	Total
	1	24	5	1	28	4
Round #2 Fact Family 7	22	9	1	9	19	Total
	24	18	20	19	26	0
Round #3 Fact Family 9	3	1	20	29	27	Total
	4	12	23	6	17	1
Round #4 Fact Family 5	16	10	12	24	6	Total
	4	17	21	1	2	1
Round #5 Fact Family 8	12	17	23	4	2	Total
	3	8	10	1	19	1

Grand Total

7

At the end of ten rolls the round is complete and players record their total points. A new round begins by rolling a new "Fact Family" with the ten-sided (0-9) die.

Play continues for five rounds. The player with the most points is the winner.

VARIATION:

Equipment: Gameboard as on previous page (see reproducibles), one decadie, one ten-sided (0-9) die

Play begins by establishing the "Fact Family" for the round as above. On each roll players roll one decadie and one ten-sided (0-9) die to make their number.

NOTE: Some numbers will be one-digit, some two-digit.

Examples of some possible rolls:

And so on…

Players play out each round as above, circling any common multiples that are rolled. Points are calculated at face value (e.g. Fact Family 7 Roll 42 = 42 points). The player with the most points after five complete rolls is the winner.

EXAMPLE:

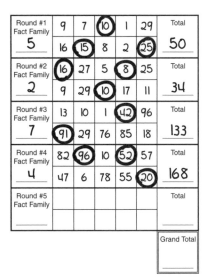

187

√RADICAL RULES:

A number is divisible by:	If:	Test with 324:
2	the ones digit is 0, 2, 4, 6, or 8 (or, it is an even number)	324: 4, an even number is in the ones place. So, 324 is divisible by 2.
3	the sum of the digits is divisible by 3	324: 3 + 2 + 4 = 9 9 is divisible by 3. So, 324 is too.
4	the number formed by the last two digits is divisible by 4	324: 24 is divisible by 4. So, 324 is too.
5	the last digit is 0 or 5	324: 4, the last digit, is no 0 or 5. So, 324 is not divisible by 5.
6	the number is divisible by 2 and by 3	324: 324 is divisible by 2. 324 is divisible by 3. So, 324 is divisible by 6.
9	the sum of the digits is divisible by 9	324: 3 + 2 + 4 = 9 9 is divisible by 9. So, 324 is too.
10	the final digit is 0	324: 4, the final digit, is not 0. So, 324 is not divisible by 10.

PRIME IT!

LEVEL: Grade 6 and up

SKILLS: Constructing factor trees and identifying the prime factors of a number (Variation: expressing prime factors in exponential form)

PLAYERS: 2 - 4

EQUIPMENT: One decadie and one ten-sided (0-9) die per player or group, gameboard (see reproducibles), plain paper, pencil

GETTING STARTED: To begin, one player rolls both dice and players record these numbers on their gameboards. All players write this number on their plain paper and begin to construct as many factor trees as possible.

EXAMPLE: Number rolled: 64 (60 + 4)

1.
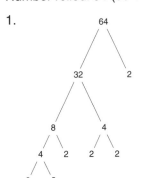

2.
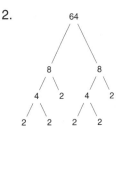

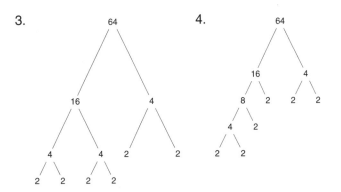

$64 = 2 \times 2 \times 2 \times 2 \times 2 \times 2$

$64 = 2^6$

189

NOTE: Because the number 64 can be factored in four different ways, this counts as four factor trees, therefore the total number of different possible factor trees for 64 is 4.

After all possible trees have been drawn, players compare, count up their total and record this on their gameboard. The total number of factor trees that the group found is also recorded.

Points are earned for each tree drawn and for writing the correct prime factor equation.

OPTIONAL: Bonus points may be earned for writing this in exponential form.

√**RADICAL RULES:** Breaking up a composite number into its prime factors can help you understand the number and compute with it.

Find the prime factorization by making a factor tree.

STEP ONE:

Express the number as a product of two numbers.

STEP TWO:

Continue to express each part of the tree as a product of two numbers until they are all prime and nothing further can be done.

PRIME AND PUNISHMENT

LEVEL: Grade 7 - 10

SKILLS: Prime factorization, addition with regrouping, problem solving

PLAYERS: 2

EQUIPMENT: Cards King - 9 (King = 0), paper, pencil (calculator optional)

GETTING STARTED: The goal of the game is to be the player with the highest accumulated total after a set period of time. To begin, each player draws three cards off the top of the deck and makes a three-digit number. Once their numbers are set, the players will be finding the unique prime factors for that number. Players must analyze their numbers carefully as their score for the round will be the sum of their number's unique prime factors.

EXAMPLE: Player One's Number: $736 = 23 \times 2 \times 2 \times 2 \times 2 \times 2$

Since 736 has two unique prime numbers of 23 and 2, their score would be $23 + 2 = 25$.

If Player One had arranged their cards to create the number 367, Player One would have built a prime number and thus would have had a score of $367 + 1 = 368$.

At the beginning of each round, players select three cards off the top of their deck, build their number and factor it. Players check each other's work for their unique primes. Once checked, players calculate the sum of their own unique primes and add this to their accumulative score.

The player with the highest accumulated score, after a set period of time is the winner.

EXAMPLE:

Round One:

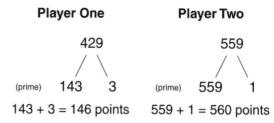

Player One

429

(prime) 143   3

143 + 3 = 146 points

Player Two

559

(prime) 559   1

559 + 1 = 560 points

Round Two:

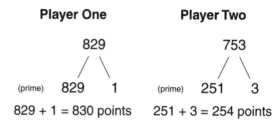

Player One

829

(prime) 829   1

829 + 1 = 830 points

Player Two

753

(prime) 251   3

251 + 3 = 254 points

After two rounds, Player One has 976 points (146 + 830) and Player Two has 814 points (560 + 254).

THOUGHT PROVOKERS:

1. What is the largest prime number a player can build with their three cards?

2. What strategy works best when arranging your cards to create a number that is prime or has high unique prime factors?

DECA PRIME SNAP

LEVEL: Grade 6 - 10

SKILLS: Prime factorization of two-digit numbers

PLAYERS: 2 of equal skill level

EQUIPMENT: One decadie, one ten-sided (0-9) die, paper, pencil

GETTING STARTED: The goal of the game is to be the first player to verbalize the prime factorization of the rolled two-digit number. To begin, one player rolls the two dice, adds them to establish the number that both players will factor in the round.

Two Dice rolled: 40, 6 = 46

Both players now begin to mentally factor this number and the first player to verbalize "Prime Snap" and give the correct prime factorization scores 1 point. Players both record the math sentence as a permanent record of their play. If the player who verbalized the prime factors correctly, they now earn 5 points. If the player was incorrect, their opponent now has the opportunity to verbalize the correct factorization and would score double points (i.e. 10 points) for this round.

To begin a new round, the dice are rolled and play continues for a set period of time. The player with the most points is the winner.

DETECTIVE LINE UP

LEVEL: Grade 6 - 9

SKILLS: Identifying and analyzing patterns

PLAYERS: 2

EQUIPMENT: Two decadice, two ten-sided (0-9) dice, two twelve-sided (1-12) dice, two twenty-sided (1-20) dice, two thirty-sided (1-30) dice, gameboard (see reproducibles), pencil

GETTING STARTED: The goal of the game is for players to analyze their rolls for patterns including: doubles, triples, quadruples, sequences and any others identified.

At the start of any turn, players must select any five dice, roll them and look for any patterns. Score using the following categories:

Any Doubles = 5 points

Two Sets of Doubles = 25 points

Triples = 15 points

Any sequence or pattern of 3 numbers = 20 points

Any sequence or pattern of 4 numbers = 50 points

Players record their numbers, what was detected, describe the pattern rule and calculate the points scored (see example).

Roll	Dice Selected	#'s Rolled	What I Found	Points
1	2 x 10 2 x deca 1 x 12	1, 2, 2, 30, 00	00, 1, 2 seq. 2, 2 doubles	20 pts. 5 pts.
2	1 x 10, 12, 20, 30 deca	4, 8, 10, 40, 26	~0~	
3	2 x deca 2 x 10 1 x 12	4, 8, 12, 20, 60	4, 8, 12 (+4 pattern)	20 pts.

TAKING INTEREST

LEVEL: Grade 7 and up

SKILLS: Calculating simple interest using a formula

PLAYERS: 2 - 4

EQUIPMENT: Cards Ace - 9 (Ace = 1), one ten-sided (0-9) die, one regular die, paper, pencil, calculator (optional)

GETTING STARTED: The goal of the game is to be the player who "pays" the least interest.

To begin, both players record on paper the following equation:

Interest = Principal x Rate x Time in Years

what you borrowed   annual interest rate   how long

In other words: I = prt

Each player now turns over three cards from the top of the deck and builds a price in dollars.

EXAMPLE: Cards: | 3 | | 8 | | 4 | = $384.00

Prior to play, players determine whether these cards can be arranged in any order.

Each player now rolls their own ten-sided (0-9) die to set the interest rate (0 is a re-roll).

EXAMPLE: Roll = 5   5% interest rate or .05

Each player then rolls their own regular die to set the time in years.

Roll = 4   4 years

Both players now insert their numbers into the equation (formula) to determine who will pay the least interest.

EXAMPLE: **Player One:**

I = $384.00 x .05 x 4 = $76.80

Player One would verbalize "I paid $384.00 plus $76.80 in interest over a four year period."

Players compare the amount of interest paid and the player who paid the least, earns 1 point for that round.

POCKET SAVINGS

LEVEL: Grade 6 - 8

SKILLS: Calculating percent (%) discount, counting mixed change

PLAYERS: 2

EQUIPMENT: Cards King - 9 (King = 0, Ace = 1), mixed coins, paper, pencil, one decadie per player, calculator (optional)

GETTING STARTED: Play begins by each player building their own price tag with the cards.

EXAMPLE:

Player One
original price

Player Two
original price

The first card represents the dollar followed by the cents. Each player now rolls their own decadie and calculates that percentage off their price tag. The player who ends up paying the least amount (least price tag after % discount) takes the amount saved in coins and pockets this into their own bank.

EXAMPLE:

Player One

Player Two

Roll: 20 %

Roll: 60 %

Save 70¢

Save $4.86

Cost Now: $2.77

Cost Now: $3.30

Player One would pay the least after figuring out the discount and would take 70¢ (their savings) in mixed change and put in into their winnings. A new round begins by making new price tags and rolling the discounts.

The player with the most money after ten rounds of play is the winner.

 **TEACHING TIP:** This is a great activity for teaching mental math strategies for calculating percent/discount and to make real life connections at the same time.

For instance if you were buying something that costs $8.50 that is now 20% off, how do you do it? Well, 10% is $.85 so double that, $1.70 off $8.50. Encourage students to verbalize how they are figuring out their discounts. This is how "shoppers" do it without a calculator in hand when they are in an actual store. Have students do the mental math before going to the calculator for assistance. Have them record and/or verbalize their strategies.

VARIATION: Play with this "rule" change. The player who rolls the discount that leads to the greatest "savings" would be the winner and would take this amount and place it into their savings. In the above example, Player Two rolled a 60% discount and saved $4.86.

WHAT PERCENT SNAP

LEVEL: Grade 7 and up

SKILLS: Calculating percent

PLAYERS: 2 of equal skill level

EQUIPMENT: Cards King - 9 (King = 0, Ace = 1), one decadie, paper, pencil, calculator (optional)

GETTING STARTED: To begin, players sit side by side and determine who will be the "dice roller" and who will be the card "flipper". At the same time, one player rolls the decadie and the other player turns up two cards off the top of the deck. The number rolled on the die indicates what percent they are to calculate of the two-digit number created by the cards.

EXAMPLE:

Roll: 30   Draw: 3   1

30% of 31 = ?

.3 x 31 = 9.3

The first player to verbalize the correct answer out loud earns 1 point. In the event of a tie (both players verbalize at the same time) then both players earn 1 point. Players can use their calculators to check for accuracy.

VARIATION: Players can silently record an estimated "guess" on paper, share their guesses verbally and then calculate on paper or by using a calculator to determine who has the correct answer. The player with the closest guess (or exact answer) earns 1 point.

TEACHING TIP: Remember a percent is like a ratio. It compares a number to one hundred. You can write a percent as a fraction or decimal because a number with a percent (%) symbol has a denominator of one hundred.

EXAMPLE:

$$24\% = \frac{24}{100} = .24$$

MAKING THE GRADE

LEVEL: Grade 7 and up

SKILLS: Calculating percent

PLAYERS: 2 - 4

EQUIPMENT: One decadie and one ten-sided (0-9) die per player, pencil, paper

GETTING STARTED: Each player rolls their decadie and ten-sided (0-9) die together to create their first number and repeat this again to create their second number. The smaller of the two numbers will be the numerator and the greater of the two will be the denominator.

EXAMPLE: Player One rolls 40 + 6 = 46 and 10 + 8 = 18

This is now recorded as 18/46 and would be verbalized as "18 out of 46".

Players must now determine what percent 18 out of 46 equals.

Player One records:

$$\frac{18}{46} = .39 \text{ or } 39\%$$

TEACHING TIP: Think of this as writing out a test score and now calculating the percent (or grade) you got on the test.

Player Two rolls 80 + 2 = 82 and 20 + 9 = 29 and records this as 29/82 and verbalizes "29 out of 82 equals 35%."

Since Player One scored 39% and it is higher than 35%, Player One earns 1 point for this round.

Play continues for ten rounds and the player with the most points wins.

TEACHING TIP: In order for players to understand percent, it may help to make a visual picture or actually draw a scale from which they can visualize.

EXAMPLE: $\frac{27}{45}$ = what percent?

0   5   10   15   20   25   30   35   40   45

50% 60%

For Scoring:

Instead of scoring 1 point per round, player takes their actual percent score

EXAMPLE:

As above 60% = 60 points

The player with the highest accumulated points after ten rounds is the winner.

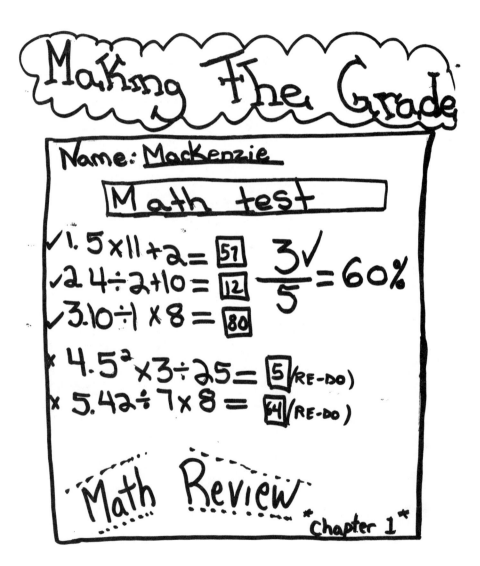

TWICE AROUND THE TRACK

(submitted by Cheri Eck)

LEVEL: Grade 10 - 12

SKILLS: Converting radian measure to degree measure

PLAYERS: 2 - 6

EQUIPMENT: Playing cards 1 - 4 and 6, paper and pencil

GETTING STARTED: The goal of the game is to convert radian measure to degree measure and be the first player to total 720 degrees. The cards are placed face down in the center of the table. The first player draws two cards, places the first card as the numerator and the second card as the denominator (Pi is understood). The player converts to degree measure and records their play. Their cards are then placed in the discard pile. Players alternate play adding their degrees onto their previous score until someone reaches or exceeds 720 degrees.

Player One's first two rounds:

numerator = 2   denominator = 6

$$\frac{2\pi}{6} = \frac{\pi}{3} = 60'$$

numerator = 3   denominator = 4

$$\frac{3\pi}{4} = 135'$$

Total degrees for player one after two rounds:

60° + 135° = 195°

VARIATION: Player must hit 720 degrees exactly. Once a player has exceeded 720 degrees, then from then they may either add or subtract their degrees with each play.

DOUBLE TIME AROUND THE TRACK

(submitted by Cheri Eck)

LEVEL: Grade 10 - 12

SKILLS: Determining the trig ratio from the radian measure on a unit circle.

PLAYERS: 2 - 6

EQUIPMENT: Playing cards 1 - 4 and 6, one regular die, one gameboard per player (see reproducibles)

GETTING STARTED: Cards are placed face down in the center of the table. The dealer draws two cards and places them as they choose on the gameboard. Simultaniously the roller rolls the die. Using the legend at the top of the gameboard, the players then determine the trig ratio rolled from the radian measure. The first player to give the correct answer earns a point. Play continues for a set period of time. The player with the most points wins.

EXAMPLE: Student Work

$$\frac{\pi}{4} = \left(\frac{1}{\sqrt{2}}, \frac{1}{\sqrt{2}} \right)$$

5 is rolled on the die.

#5 is secant.

Secant $\frac{\pi}{4}$ = $\sqrt{2}$

First player to say $\sqrt{2}$ wins a point.

1 = Sine
2 = Cosine
3 = Tangent
4 = Cosecant
5 = Secant
6 = Cotangent

Section X

Reproducibles

ROLL ON... DECIMALS

Roll Number	Ones	Tenths 10ths	Hundredths 100ths	Thousandths 1000ths	Running Total		
1	•						
2	•				+	=	
3	•				+	=	
4	•				+	=	
5	•				+	=	

difference from whole number   (+/-)

DECI-DECA

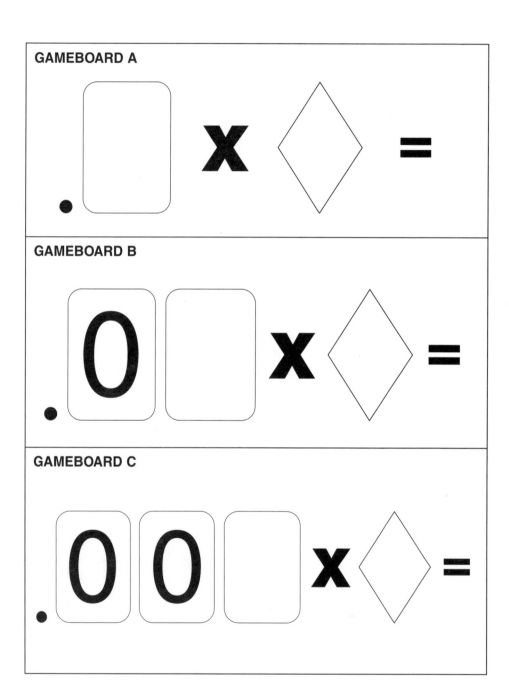

A TARGET ROUND

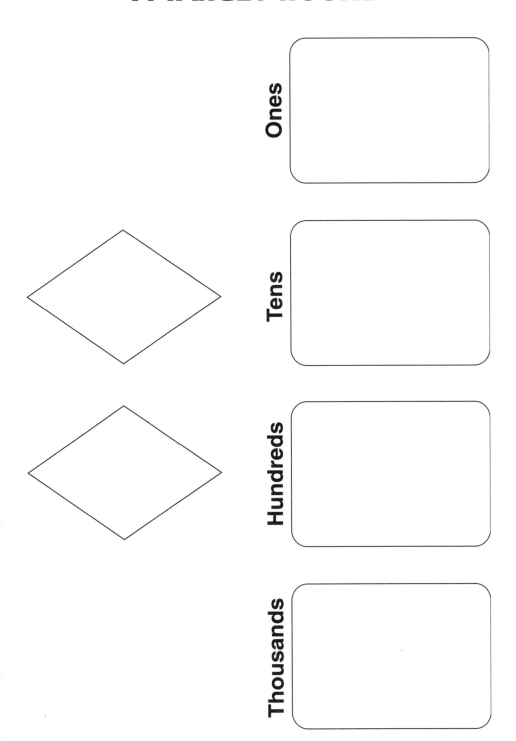

A TARGET ROUND VARIATION

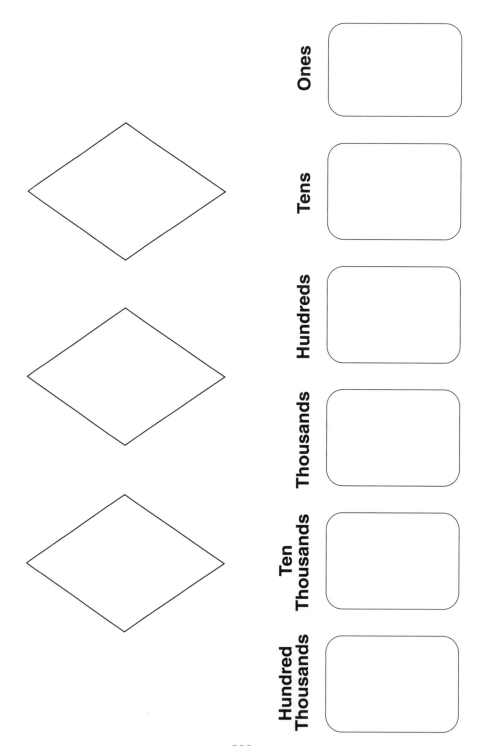

TO SUM IT UP /
WHAT'S THE DIFFERENCE?

ADDITION:

SUBTRACTION:

NO
NEGATIVE
NUMBERS
ALLOWED

MULTIPLICATION:

DIVISION:

NOTE: Any boards could include decimals.

GET BACK TO ZERO!

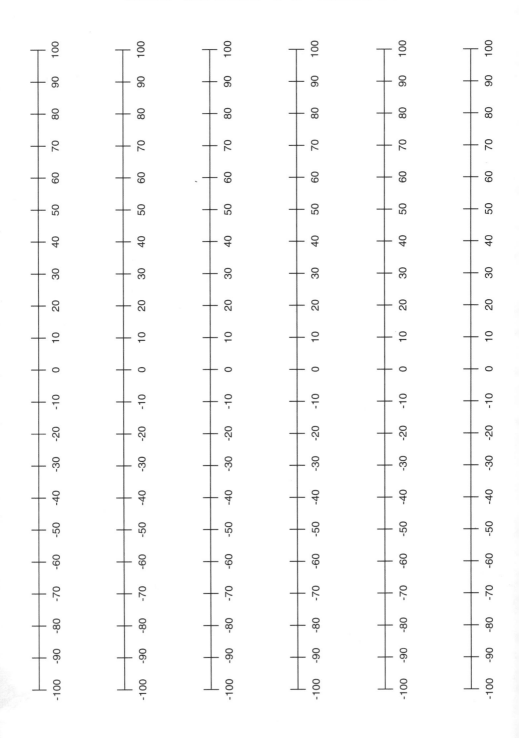

THREE FOR ME

×	1	2	3	4	5	6	7	8	9	10	11	12
1	1	2	3	4	5	6	7	8	9	10	11	12
2	2	4	6	8	10	12	14	16	18	20	22	24
3	3	6	9	12	15	18	21	24	27	30	33	36
4	4	8	12	16	20	24	28	32	36	40	44	48
5	5	10	15	20	25	30	35	40	45	50	55	60
6	6	12	18	24	30	36	42	48	54	60	66	72
7	7	14	21	28	35	42	49	56	63	70	77	84
8	8	16	24	32	40	48	56	64	72	80	88	96
9	9	18	27	36	45	54	63	72	81	90	99	108
10	10	20	30	40	50	60	70	80	90	100	110	120
11	11	22	33	44	55	66	77	88	99	110	121	132
12	12	24	36	48	60	72	84	96	108	120	132	144

MULTIPLICATION SCRAMBLE

	Player One	Player Two
0 - 9	_____	_____
10 - 19	_____	_____
20 - 29	_____	_____
30 - 39	_____	_____
40 - 49	_____	_____
50 - 59	_____	_____
60 - 69	_____	_____
70 - 79	_____	_____
80 - 89	_____	_____
90 - 99	_____	_____
100 - 109	_____	_____
110 - 119	_____	_____
120 - 129	_____	_____
130 - 139	_____	_____
140 - 149	_____	_____

	Player One	Player Two
0 - 9	_____	_____
10 - 19	_____	_____
20 - 29	_____	_____
30 - 39	_____	_____
40 - 49	_____	_____
50 - 59	_____	_____
60 - 69	_____	_____
70 - 79	_____	_____
80 - 89	_____	_____
90 - 99	_____	_____
100 - 109	_____	_____
110 - 119	_____	_____
120 - 129	_____	_____
130 - 139	_____	_____
140 - 149	_____	_____

FOOTBALL FACTOR

Player Two

	Touchdown	Field Goal	Total
1st Quarter			
2nd Quarter			
3rd Quarter			
4th Quarter			

Total Football Score

Player Two

	Touchdown	Field Goal	Total
1st Quarter			
2nd Quarter			
3rd Quarter			
4th Quarter			

Total Football Score

Player One

	Touchdown	Field Goal	Total
1st Quarter			
2nd Quarter			
3rd Quarter			
4th Quarter			

Total Football Score

Player One

	Touchdown	Field Goal	Total
1st Quarter			
2nd Quarter			
3rd Quarter			
4th Quarter			

Total Football Score

RED RACERS CHALLENGER

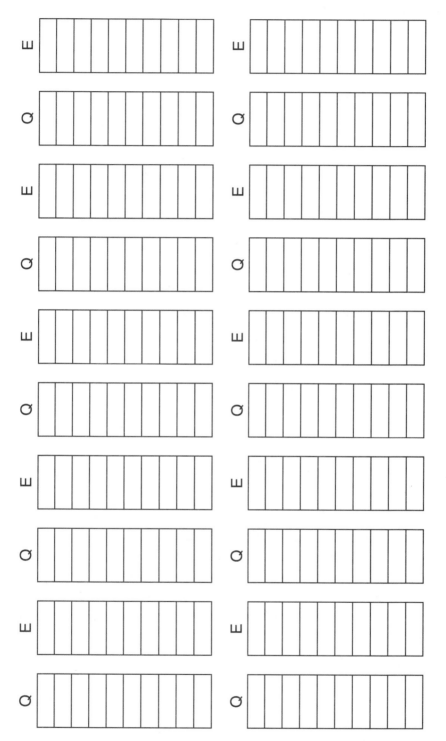

DIVISION DECISION

1	2	3	4	5	6	7	8	9	10
11	12	13	14	15	16	17	18	19	20
21	22	23	24	25	26	27	28	29	30
31	32	33	34	35	36	37	38	39	40
41	42	43	44	45	46	47	48	49	50
51	52	53	54	55	56	57	58	59	60
61	62	63	64	65	66	67	68	69	70
71	72	73	74	75	76	77	78	79	80
81	82	83	84	85	86	87	88	89	90
91	92	93	94	95	96	97	98	99	100

MATH FOOTBALL

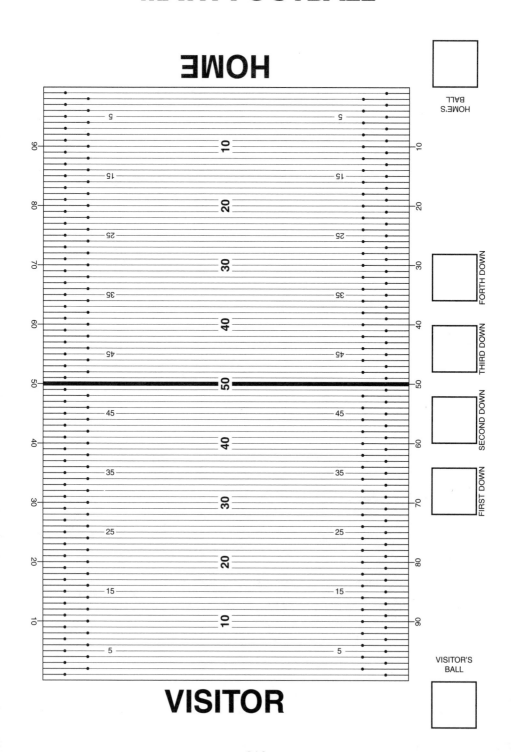

216

DECADE DIVISION

1. Estimated Answer _____

   Actual Answer _____

2. Estimated Answer _____

   Actual Answer _____

3. Estimated Answer _____

   Actual Answer _____

4. Estimated Answer _____

   Actual Answer _____

5. Estimated Answer _____

   Actual Answer _____

6. Estimated Answer _____

   Actual Answer _____

7. Estimated Answer _____

   Actual Answer _____

8. Estimated Answer _____

   Actual Answer _____

9. Estimated Answer _____

   Actual Answer _____

10. Estimated Answer _____

    Actual Answer _____

11. Estimated Answer _____

    Actual Answer _____

12. Estimated Answer _____

    Actual Answer _____

13. Estimated Answer _____

    Actual Answer _____

14. Estimated Answer _____

    Actual Answer _____

15. Estimated Answer _____

    Actual Answer _____

16. Estimated Answer _____

    Actual Answer _____

MIXED UP TIC TAC TOE /
MULTI OPERATION BLACKOUT

1	2	3	4	5	6	7	8	9	10
11	12	13	14	15	16	17	18	19	20
21	22	23	24	25	26	27	28	29	30
31	32	33	34	35	36	37	38	39	40
41	42	43	44	45	46	47	48	49	50
51	52	53	54	55	56	57	58	59	60
61	62	63	64	65	66	67	68	69	70
71	72	73	74	75	76	77	78	79	80
81	82	83	84	85	86	87	88	89	90
91	92	93	94	95	96	97	98	99	100

GOT IT / CLOSEST TO!

	TARGET	NUMBER	EVALUATE
1			
2			
3			
4			
5			
6			
7			
8			
9			
10			

COMMIT AND CAPTURE

1. $\square \times (\square - \square) - \square =$

2. $\square + \square \times \square \div \square =$

3. $\square^2 - \square \times \square - \square =$

4. $\square + \square \div \square \times \square =$

5. $\square \times (\square + \square) - \square =$

6. $\square [\square^3 \times (\square - \square)] =$

7. $\square \div \square + \square \times \square =$

8. $\square \div \square \times \square - \square =$

BINOMIAL CROSS OVERS / LINEAR KNOCK OFFS

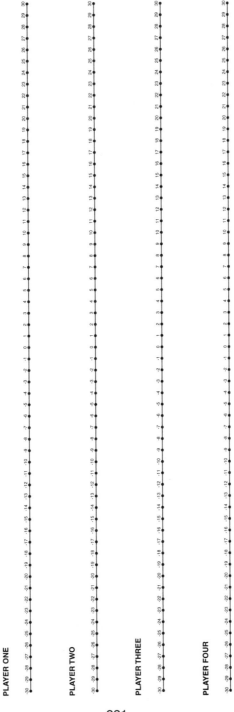

GIVE ME FIVE

1	2	3	4	5	6	7	8	9	10
11	12	13	14	15	16	17	18	19	20
21	22	23	24	25	26	27	28	29	30
31	32	33	34	35	36	37	38	39	40
41	42	43	44	45	46	47	48	49	50
51	52	53	54	55	56	57	58	59	60
61	62	63	64	65	66	67	68	69	70
71	72	73	74	75	76	77	78	79	80
81	82	83	84	85	86	87	88	89	90
91	92	93	94	95	96	97	98	99	100

ALGEBRA MATH FOOTBALL

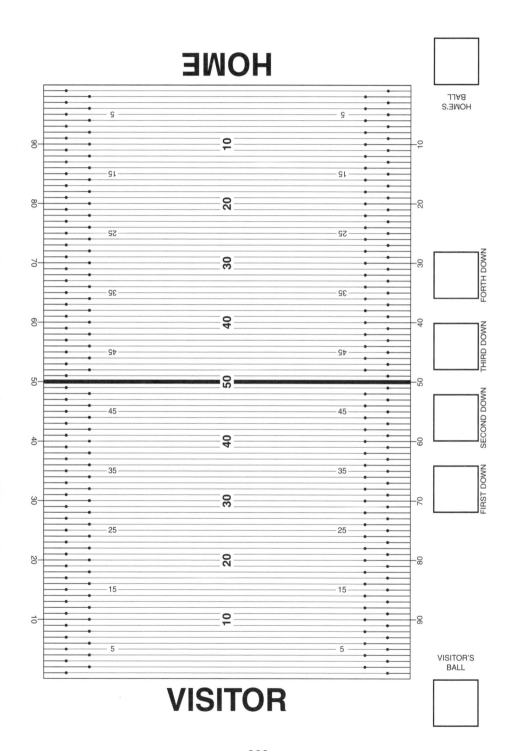

223

MILLIMETRE MAZE

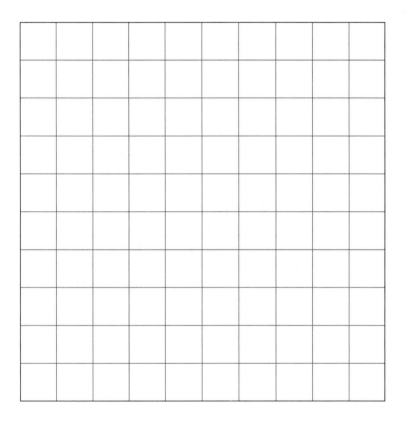

GET TO YOUR CORNER! /
PLOTTING ALONG

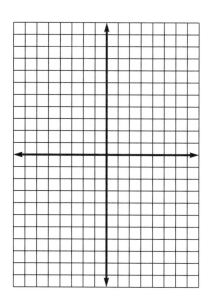

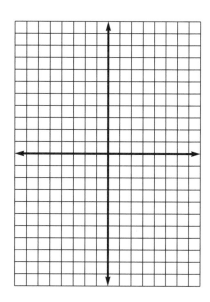

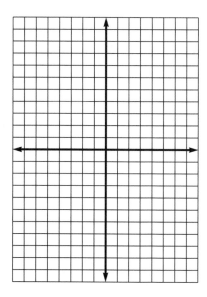

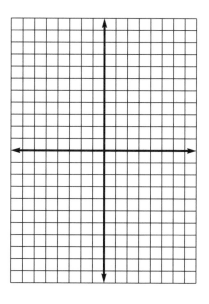

ROLLER COASTER

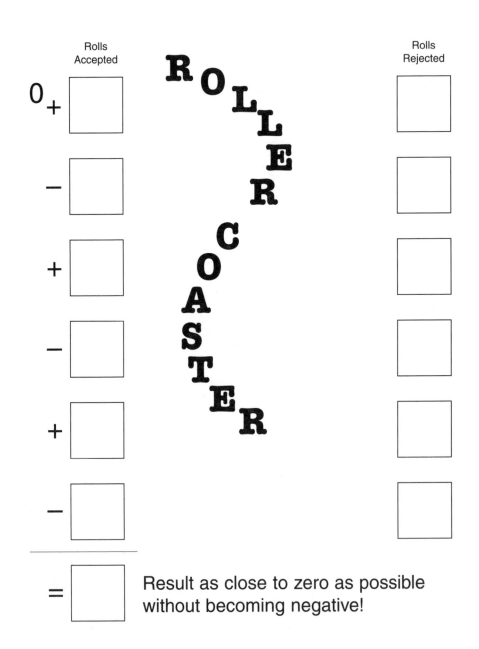

Rolls Accepted

Rolls Rejected

$0 +$

$-$

$+$

$-$

$+$

$-$

$=$ Result as close to zero as possible without becoming negative!

100 WIPE OUT

	Rolls Accepted	Rolls Rejected
100 -	☐	☐
=	☐	
-	☐	☐
=	☐	
-	☐	☐
=	☐	
-	☐	☐
=	☐	
-	☐	☐
=	☐	Total closest to 0 as possible

GRAPHING OPERATIONS

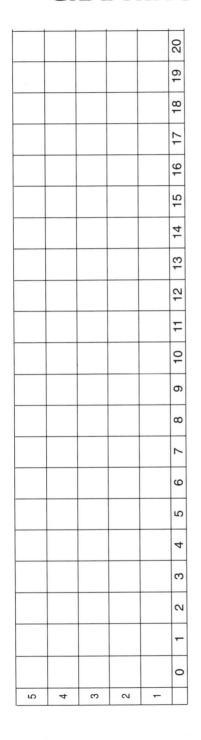

228

BIG SUMS

Sample #	Our Prediction	Sum	+ / - on Prediction
1			
2			
3			
4			
5			
6			
7			
8			
9			
10			

THE SUM OF 36 DICE

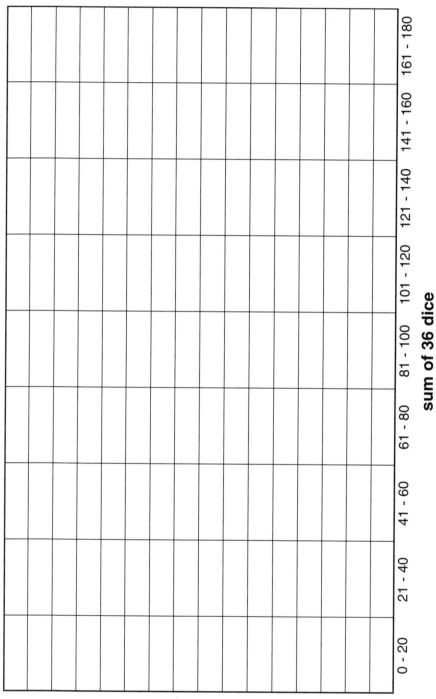

sum of 36 dice

# of samples

TARGET ZERO

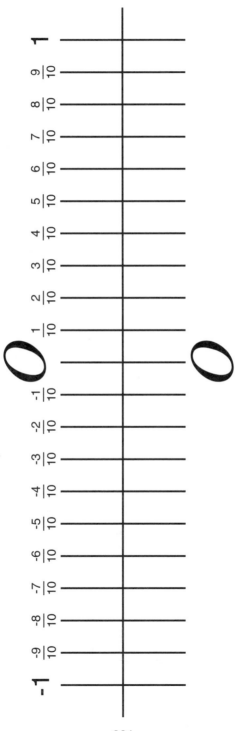

BEAT MR. MATHJACK / FRACTION GET BACK

$\dfrac{1}{2}$	$\dfrac{1}{2}$	$\dfrac{1}{12}$	$\dfrac{1}{12}$	$\dfrac{1}{3}$
$\dfrac{1}{3}$	$\dfrac{1}{3}$	$\dfrac{1}{4}$	$\dfrac{1}{4}$	$\dfrac{1}{4}$
$\dfrac{2}{4}$	$\dfrac{1}{6}$	$\dfrac{1}{6}$	$\dfrac{1}{6}$	$\dfrac{3}{6}$
$\dfrac{1}{12}$	$\dfrac{1}{12}$	$\dfrac{1}{12}$	$\dfrac{1}{12}$	$\dfrac{1}{12}$
$\dfrac{1}{12}$	$\dfrac{1}{12}$	$\dfrac{1}{12}$	$\dfrac{6}{12}$	$\dfrac{6}{12}$

FRACTION GET BACK

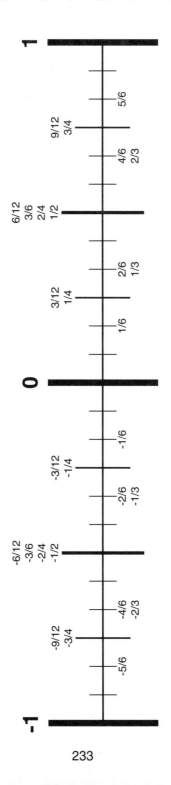

MULTIPLES TO THE END

Round #1 Fact Family _____						Total _____

Round #2 Fact Family _____						Total _____

Round #3 Fact Family _____						Total _____

Round #4 Fact Family _____						Total _____

Round #5 Fact Family _____						Total _____

Grand Total
_____

PRIME IT!

Decadice	+ 10-sided dice	= Number	$\dfrac{\text{\# of Trees Found}}{\text{\# of Trees Total}}$	Prime Factors

DETECTIVE LINE UP

My Numbers...	I detected...	My Score...

SCORING SYSTEM

1. DOUBLES   1 set = _____

          2 sets = _____

2. TRIPLES = _____

3. 4 OF A KIND = _____

4. PLUS 10, 20 OR 30 PATTERN

     with 3 dice = _____

     with 4 dice = _____

5. MULTIPLE PATTERNS = _____

DOUBLE TIME
AROUND THE TRACK

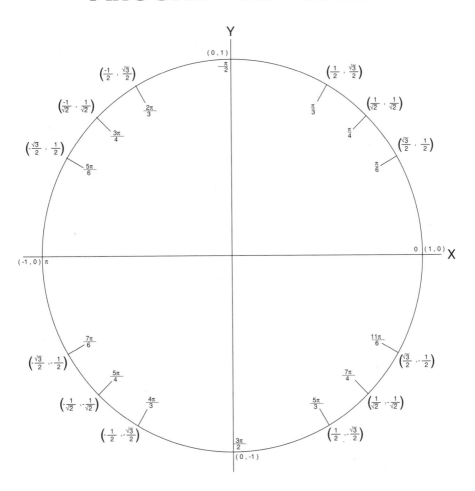

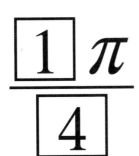

1 = Sine	
2 = Cosine	
3 = Tangent	
4 = Cosecant	
5 = Secant	
6 = Cotangent	

Appendix of Skills

box cars and one-eyed jacks®

About the Authors

The BOX CARS & ONE-EYED JACKS team of Joanne Currah and Jane Felling bring both innovation and inspiration to their consulting. They have combined expertise in elementary and special education and have conducted extensive research into the area of Games as a Teaching Strategy.

The authors developed all of the games for BOX CARS AND ONE-EYED JACKS Volume I "Shuffling Into Math" while teaching in their classrooms. Since the original publication in 1989, the authors have been successfully inservicing across Canada, the United States, Europe, Australia and Asia.

In 1991 BOX CARS won a National Award from the Learning Disabilities Association.

During 1992 BOX CARS Volume II "All Hands on Deck" and Volume III "Dice Works" were published to meet the growing demand by teachers and parents for new material. Their math books and manipulatives were intended for Kindergarten to Grade 7 and incorporated the use of cards, dice, and special ten, twelve, twenty, and thirty-sided dice. In 1994 "Money Matters for Kids" (Canadian Version) and "Rolling In The Dough" (American Version) Volumes IV and Volume V "Math Attack with 30-Sided Dice" were published. Volumes I, II, and III reached National Best Selling status in 1994!!

"On a Roll to Spelling", published in 1995 led the authors in a brand new direction with their games. Eagerly awaited by both teachers and parents, "On a Roll to Spelling" quickly became a favourite! This volume incorporated the use of alphabet dice and letter tiles and was designed to put the fun back into Spelling! Stratedice came next. Stratedice is a unique tray of 36 dice and gamebook. It also was published in 1995 and has reached Best Selling status.

In 1996 "Radical Math" Junior High and High School Games was published with the co-author, Norma LaChance. The authors were pleased that their games and ideas were now extended across the grades.

"Piece it Together with Fractions" was completed in 1997. This games book comes with special fraction dice and manipulatives that make fractions fun and easy to understand. A new tactile spelling games book, "Spelling Rules... With These Cool Tools!" came next and was a great addition to the language games. , Decadice was completed in 2000. This games book is an author favourite as it includes numerous "Thought Provokers" to challenge game players of all ages.

The authors marked 2001 with the publication of Radical Math - Millennium Edition. It was a most challenging and rewarding project for them both!

YOU'LL BE IN PRO. D "PAIR-A-DICE" WITH OUR NEWEST WORKSHOPS

BOX CARS & ONE-EYED JACKS BASIC MATH GAMES WORKSHOP
LEVELS: K-3, 4-6, 7-9, Special Education

Participants will play a selection of math games from the award winning Box Cars & One Eyed Jacks series. The workshop will focus on basic card and regular dice games and will cover ideas for teaching numeration, mental math, all operations, place value, graphing, data gathering, cooperative games, integers and more. Strategies are provided throughout. Problem solving is integrated into the games and can be adapted to suit the needs of all students to complement any existing math program. Ideas for resource and classroom management will be provided as well as great ideas for math journals. Get back to the basics. Come prepared to play!

PROBABILITY FUN 'DIE' MENTALS
LEVELS: K-3, 4-6, 7-9, Special Education

Wondering how to teach the probability strand in the new curriculum? Odds are... you'll have fun learning probability concepts, patterns, problem solving, mental math strategies and more through math games using regular and multi-sided dice. The newest probability games from the award winning Box Cars & One-Eyed Jacks series will be played. Classroom and resource management tips will also be provided. Come prepared to shake, rattle and roll!

"ON A ROLL" LITERACY AND SPELLING GAMES
LEVELS: K-3, 4-6, 7-9, Special Education, E.S.I.

Participants play a selection of spelling and language games that use special 30-sided alphabet dice and letter tiles that stick and stack. These unique manipulatives make spelling and language play multi-sensory and fun! Come prepared to play and learn strategies for letter recognition, sound/symbol relationships, spelling simple/complex words, puzzlers, word games and more. All new games from "Spelling Rules with These Cool Tools" featuring letter tile games will be taught.

ROLLING IN THE DOUGH - BOX CARS MONEY GAMES FOR KIDS
LEVELS: K-4, 5-9, Special Education

Kids love money and they love games. So it seemed natural to pair the Box Cars Math Game format with the teaching of money concepts. Come prepared to play new card and dice games that teach money concepts, problem solving, probability and the operations. Whole class activities to teach real life connections will also be shared. Participants need to bring assorted change to this session. Come prepared to play.

DECADICE FOR THE NEW MILLENNIUM
LEVELS: K-7, Special Education

These 10-sided decade dice are awesome when combined with playing cards for learning math skills. This newest workshop and book features excellent whole class warmup game activities, ideas for introducing and reinforcing place value with other manipulatives and extensions for the data management strand. Game players learn strategies for probability, all operations, place value, graphing, fractions, patterns and more. Excellent brain-teasing "Thought Provokers" for journal writing are provided throughout the workshop, so be sure to come with a full deck!

PIECE IT TOGETHER WITH FRACTIONS
LEVELS: 1-3, 4-6, 7-9, Special Education

The Box Cars authors have done it again! Come prepared to play with unique fraction dice and fraction circles. Games to teach fraction names, comparing fractions, operations with fractions, equivalence, and more will be taught. These manipulatives and our newest games will bring fraction concepts to life for your students in a meaningful hands-on way. We teach the concepts through play which helps develop the understanding before the algorithms are introduced.

BOX CARS RADICAL MATH
Middle Years: 5 - 9 or 7 - 9, Special Education

An interactive games workshop using cards, dice and multi-sided dice with a "back to basics" approach. By combining games and problem solving teachers are able to maintain high interest even from the low level student. Areas covered include integers, place value, decimals, operations, order of operation, probability and problem solving.

IF MATH IS A GAME HERE ARE THE RULES...
LEVELS: K-3, 4-6, 7-9

When dealing with math you want your students playing with a full deck. This workshop focuses on the best of the Box Cars "Back To Basics" games that help develop mastery of the operations. Come play with cards, dice and multi-sided dice and learn all kinds of tips, tricks and strategies for mastering all operations. The games appeal to all learning styles and compliment any math program. Get "back to the basics" and experience the power of games for developing understanding, proficiency and confidence in your students.

BOX CARS SCHOOL VISITS / MODEL LESSONS
LEVELS: Elementary - Junior High (Middle Years)

Consultants visit a school for a day and teach as many students as possible. Teachers watch, play and learn strategies right along with their "real students" and experience how it works. Strategies for classroom management and organization are brought to life for teachers who can immediately follow up the visit with implementation. Parents can be invited and participate right along with their children. The entire school community benefits. This workshop is often combined with a Family Math Night.

FAMILY MATH NIGHTS
LEVELS: K-3, 4-6, 7-9

Have parents and students come and play a wide variety of math games that use cards and dice from the award winning Box Cars & One-Eyed Jacks series. During the workshop families will play a wide variety of games to review and strengthen math concepts. Great ideas and strategies will be taught to help students learn the basics. Games are a fun way to provide homework support to your parents and build success and self-esteem for your students. Get your community shake, rattle and rolling with this excellent workshop.

box cars and one-eyed jacks®

TO BOOK YOUR WORKSHOP CALL: (780) 440-MATH   FAX: (780) 440-1619
6516 - 68 Avenue NW, Edmonton, Alberta, T6B 3M3 Canada Toll Free: (866) DICE FUN
Website: boxcarsandoneeyedjacks.com / Email: boxcars@planet.eon.net

box cars and one-eyed jacks®

2005 🍁 PRICE LIST

6516 - 68 Avenue NW
Edmonton, Alberta, T6B 3M3 Canada
Phone: (780) 440-MATH
Fax: (780) 440-1619
Toll Free: (866) DICE FUN
Website: boxcarsandoneeyedjacks.com
Email: boxcars@planet.eon.net

CODE	BOOKS			QUANTITY	TOTAL
B-01	Shuffling Into Math Vol. I	K-3	$21.95		
B-02	All Hands On Deck Vol. II	1-9	$21.95		
B-03	Dice Works Vol. III (comes with 6 multi-sided dice)	K-9	$23.95		
B-04	Money Matters for Kids Vol. IV	K-9	$21.95		
B-05	Math Attack Vol. V (comes with 4 x 30-sided dice)	K-9	$24.95		
B-06	On a Roll to Spelling... and More Vol. VI (comes with 2 alphabet dice)	K-6	$22.95		
B-08	Piece It Together With Fractions Vol. VIII (comes with 7 fraction dice, one 12-sided number die, one mini deck of cards and a 51 piece deluxe fraction set)	1-9	$35.95		
B-09	Decadice Vol. IX (comes with 4 decade dice and 4 x 10-sided dice)	1-9	$26.95		
B-10	Radical Math - Millennium Edition Vol. X (comes with 12 multi-sided dice)	7-12	$34.95		
B-11	Spelling Rules with These Cool Tools (comes with 2 alphabet dice and a set of 60 alphabet tiles)	K-7	$18.95		
B-12	Box Cars version française (French only) (comes with 6 multi-sided dice)	K-9	$24.00		
B-13	Double Dare You (NEW) (comes with 11 double dice)	1-7	$20.95		

CODE	OVERHEAD TRANSPARENCIES / MATERIALS		QUANTITY	TOTAL
OH-01	Set of Black and Red Overheads (includes 4 sheets = 84 cards total) Ace-King	$10.00		
OH-02	Set of Black and Red Overheads to Match Special Decks (with 0, 1, 11, 12's) (includes 4 sheets = 84 cards total)	$10.00		
OH-03	Money Overheads (includes 2 sheets of all coins - 135 total/ grey & copper)	$5.00		
OH-05	Deluxe Overhead Fraction Circles (51 pieces)	$12.00		
OH-06	Overhead Alphabet Tiles (26 lowercase)	$8.95		
OH-11	Overhead Spinners (set of 3) simulates regular dice rolls 2-36 and fractions (NEW)	$7.95		

CODE	PLAYING CARDS	QUANTITY	TOTAL
C-01	Special "Mini" Deck $2.50 each or 5 decks/$10.00 with 0, 1, 11, 12's		
C-02	Special Large Floor Demonstration Deck $12.00 with 0, 1, 11, 12's - 7" x 4-3/4"		
C-03	Regular Large Floor Demonstration Deck - 7" x 4-3/4" $12.00		
C-04	Sight Word Deck $3.50 each or 10 decks/$30.00 (contains 52 cards for use with Spelling is the Game... Here are the Rules)		

CODE	DICE	QUANTITY	TOTAL
D-01	Regular Dice 5 / $1.00		
D-02	Manipulite Quiet Dice $1.00 / pair, $10.00 / 12 pairs, $20.00 / 25 pairs, $27.00 / 36 pairs		
D-03	10-Sided (0-9) Spotted Dice $1.00 / die		
D-04	10-Sided (00, 10, 20...90) Decade Dice $1.00 / die, $1.50 / pair		
D-05	10-Sided (0-9) Dice $1.00 / die, $1.50 / pair		
D-06	12-Sided (1-12) Dice $1.00 / die, $1.50 / pair		
D-07	20-Sided (1-20) Dice $1.00 / die, $1.50 / pair		
D-08	10-Sided Large Demo Decade Dice (00, 10, 20... 90) $2.00 / die, $3.00 / pair		
D-09	10-Sided (0-9) Large Demo Dice $2.00 / die, $3.00 / pair		
D-10	12-Sided (1-12) Large Demo Dice $2.00 / die, $3.00 / pair		
D-11	20-Sided (1-20) Large Demo Dice $2.00 / die, $3.00 / pair		
D-12	30-Sided (1-30) Dice $2.00 / die, $3.00 / pair		
D-13	6-Sided (0-5) Dice $1.00 / die, $1.50 / pair		
D-14	Operation 2F (+ -) Dice $1.00 / die, $1.50 / pair		
D-15	Operation 4F (+ - x ÷) Dice $1.00 / die, $1.50 / pair		
D-16	Fraction Dice set of 7 / $5.00		
D-17	Large Coin Die $5.00 / die		
D-18	Blank Dice $0.75 / die, $1.00 / pair		
D-19	Alphabet Dice (30-sided) $2.50 / die, $4.00 / pair		
D-20	Large Floor Demo Dice $4.50 / pair		
OH-07	Overhead Spotted (1-6) Dice $7.50 / pair		
OH-08	Overhead Fraction Dice $7.50 / pair		
OH-09	Overhead Numeral (1-6) Dice $7.50 / pair		

CODE	STRATEDICE	QUANTITY	TOTAL
S-01	Stratedice 1 - 9 $17.95 (comes with gamebook, tray and 36 dice)		
S-02	Stratedice tray and 36 dice (only) 1 - 9 $9.95		
S-03	Stratedice Mini Kit 1 - 9 $31.95 (comes with gamebook, 3 trays and 108 dice)		

CODE	MISCELLANEOUS	QUANTITY	TOTAL
M-01	Spelling is the Game... Here are the Rules (game booklet, word cards, 1 alpha die and 60 tiles) $12.95 / set		
	Alphabet Tiles		
M-02	120 Upper case $10.00 or 2/$15.00		
M-03	120 Lower case $10.00 or 2/$15.00		
M-04	60 Blends & more $10.00 or 2/$15.00		
M-05	Puzzle Island (spelling-story book) 1-6 $12.95		
M-06	Alpha-Deck Cards (2 decks) K-3 $9.95		
M-07	Alpha-Deck Games Book K-3 $12.95		
M-08	Alpha-Deck Cards and Book Set K-3 $19.95		
M-09	Canadian Coins Plastic pennies - nickels, dimes, quarters, loonies and twoonies (135 coins total) $10.50		
M-10	Bingo Chips Stock Colours (200/pkg.) $2.50 or 6/$12.00		
M-11	Math Packs ($4.95 ea for class sets of 30+) $6.95 or 2/$12.00		
M-12	Deluxe Dice "Collectors" Puzzle 500 pieces PRICE REDUCED $9.95		
D-21	Classroom Set of 30 Large Floor Demo Dice (indented dots only, not printed) $45.00 / set		
M-13	Deluxe Fraction Circles (51 pieces) $12.00 or 2/$20.00		

CODE	NEW DICE	QUANTITY	TOTAL
OH-10	Overhead Operations (+ - x ÷ > =) Dice $7.50 / pair		
D-22	Regular Double Dice $1.00 / die, $1.50 / pair		
D-23	Three-In-A-Cube Dice $1.50 / die, $2.50 / pair		
D-24	10-Sided (0-9) Double Dice $1.50 / die, $2.50 / pair		
D-25	Manipulite Numeral (1-6) Dice set of 6 / $3.00		
D-26	Decimal Dice $1.00 / die, $1.50 / pair		
D-27	Positive/Negative (1-6) Dice $1.50 / pair		
D-28	Solving For "X" Algebra Dice $1.00 / die, $1.50 / pair		
D-29	Money Dice $1.00 / die, $1.50 / pair		
D-30	Japanese/Chinese Dice $1.00 / die, $1.50 / pair		
D-31	5 W's Question Dice $1.00 / die, $1.50 / pair		
D-32	Parts of Speech Dice $1.00 / die, $1.50 / pair		
D-33	Exponential Algebra Dice (x^0, x^1, x^2) $1.00 / die, $1.50 / pair		
D-34	10-Sided 100's Dice $1.00 / die, $1.50 / pair		
D-35	10-Sided 1000's Dice $1.00 / die, $1.50 / pair		
D-36	Regular Double Demo Dice $2.00 / die, $3.00 / pair		

CODE	NEW PRODUCTS	QUANTITY	TOTAL
M-17	White Board Attachable Pen Erasers $5.95 (4 pack large)		
M-18	Power of Ten Class Set $99.95		
M-19	Power of Ten Learning Assistance Kit $54.95		
M-19a	Place Value Cards Demo Set 11" x 4" (00 - 1000's) $23.95		
M-19b	Ten Frame Demo Deck $15.95		
M-19c	Place Value Cards (15 student sets) $39.95		
M-20	Power of Ten Multiplication/ Division Book $19.95		
M-21	Power of Ten Addition CD $34.95		
M-22	Xtreme Math Football Basic Kit $34.95		
M-23	Xtreme Math Football Class Kit $119.95		
M-24	Xtreme Math Soccer Basic Kit $34.95		
M-25	Xtreme Math Soccer Class Kit $119.95		
M-26	Bump Card Game (addition, subtraction, integers) $12.95		
M-27a	Original Eye Spy Bag $19.95		
M-27b	Counting / Numbers $19.95		
M-27c	Language Learning $19.95		
M-27d	ABC's $19.95		

CLASSROOM KITS

	QUANTITY	TOTAL

KT-01 BASIC PRIMARY KIT

Shuffling Into Math Vol. I	$ 21.95
50 Regular Dice	$ 10.00
10 Decks of Special Mini Cards (0 - 12)	$ 20.00
Special Large Floor Demonstration Deck	$ 12.00
Large Floor Demo Dice	$ 4.50
Math Pack	$ 6.95
Total Retail	$ 75.40
Kit Price	$ 69.95

SAVE OVER $5⁰⁰

KT-02 BASIC INTERMEDIATE KIT

All Hands On Deck Vol. II	$ 21.95
50 Regular Dice	$ 10.00
10 Decks of Special Mini Cards (0 - 12)	$ 20.00
Overhead Cards	$ 10.00
Overhead Spotted Dice	$ 7.50
Math Pack	$ 6.95
Total Retail	$ 76.40
Kit Price	$ 69.95

SAVE OVER $6⁰⁰

KT-03 RADICAL MATH MILLENNIUM KIT

Radical Math Millennium Edition Vol. X	
(with 12 multi-sided dice)	$ 34.95
50 Regular Dice	$ 10.00
10 Decks of Special Mini Cards (0 - 12)	$ 20.00
Overhead Cards	$ 10.00
Overhead Spotted Dice	$ 7.50
Multi-Sided Dice:	
(0-9) Numbers x 12	$ 9.00
(1-12) Numbers x 12	$ 9.00
(1-20) Numbers x 12	$ 9.00
(1-30) Numbers x 12	$ 18.00
(00-90) Decade Dice x 12	$ 9.00
Total Retail	$ 136.45
Kit Price	$ 128.95

SAVE $7⁵⁰

KT-04 DECADICE KIT

Decadice Vol. IX (with 8 multi-sided dice)	$ 26.95
Multi-Sided Dice:	
(0-9) Numbers x 16	$ 12.00
(00-90) Decade Dice x 16	$ 12.00
10-Sided (0-9) Lg. Demo Dice x 2	$ 3.00
10-Sided (00-90) Lg. Demo Decade Dice x 2	$ 3.00
Total Retail	$ 56.95
Kit Price	$ 49.95

SAVE $7⁰⁰

KT-05 SPELLING KIT

On a Roll to Spelling... and More Vol. VI	
(with 2 alphabet dice)	$ 22.95
Spelling Rules with These Cool Tools (book only)	$ 12.00
14 Extra Alphabet Dice	$ 28.00
8 Packages of Alphabet Tiles - set pricing includes	
3 upper, 3 lower & 2 blend combo packages...	$ 60.00
Overhead Alphabet Tiles	$ 8.95
Puzzle Island	$ 12.95
Kit Price	$ 144.85

BONUS!!

> *RECEIVE THREE DECKS OF SIGHT WORD CARDS AND "SPELLING IS THE GAME" BOOKLET - $13.50 VALUE*

KT-06 MONEY MATTERS KIT

Money Matters Vol. IV	$ 21.95
Money Overheads	$ 5.00
Large Coin Die	$ 5.00
Overhead Spotted Dice	$ 7.50
3 Packages of Canadian Coins (135 each)	$ 31.50
Kit Price	$ 70.95

BONUS!!

> *RECEIVE ONE SET OF 6 REUSABLE GAMEBOARDS & 4 MONEY DICE - $6.00 VALUE!*

	QUANTITY	TOTAL

KT-07 FRACTION KIT

Piece It Together With Fractions Vol. VIII	
(with 7 fraction dice, one 12-sided number die,	
one mini deck of cards and a 51 piece deluxe	
fraction set)	$ 35.95
5 Sets of Deluxe Fraction Circles, Fraction Dice,	
Cards, 12-sided Dice	$ 91.50
1 Deluxe Overhead Fraction Circle Set	$ 12.00
Overhead Fraction Dice	$ 7.50
Kit Price	$ 146.95

BONUS!!

> *RECEIVE A BONUS OF EXTRA FRACTION DICE - $10.00 VALUE!*

KT-08 STRATEDICE CLASSROOM KIT

Gamebook, tray and 36 dice	$ 17.95
14 trays and 504 dice	$ 139.30
Total Retail	$ 157.25
Kit Price	$ 145.00

SAVE $12²⁵

KT-09 DELUXE PRIMARY KIT

Box Cars & One-Eyed Jacks Vol. I, II, III, IV, IX	$ 116.75
Overhead Cards	$ 10.00
Large Floor Demo Deck & Special Demo Deck	$ 24.00
15 Decks of Special Mini Cards (0 - 12)	$ 30.00
6 Packages of Bingo Chips	$ 12.00
50 Regular Dice	$ 10.00
Multi-Sided Dice:	
(0-5) Dice x 20	$ 15.00
(0-9) Spotted x 20	$ 20.00
(0-9) Numbers x 20	$ 15.00
(1-12) Numbers x 20	$ 15.00
(1-20) Numbers x 20	$ 15.00
(1-30) Numbers x 10	$ 15.00
(00-90) Decade Dice x 20	$ 15.00
Operation 4F (+ - x ÷) x 6	$ 4.50
Large Floor Demo Dice	$ 4.50
Kit Price	$ 321.75

BONUS!!

> *RECEIVE A BONUS - $34.50 VALUE*

KT-10 DELUXE INTERMEDIATE KIT

Box Cars & One-Eyed Jacks Vol. II, III, IV, V, IX	$ 119.75
Overhead Cards	$ 10.00
15 Decks of Special Mini Cards (0 - 12)	$ 30.00
6 Packages of Bingo Chips	$ 12.00
50 Regular Dice	$ 10.00
Overhead Spotted Dice	$ 7.50
Multi-Sided Dice:	
(0-9) Numbers x 30	$ 22.50
(1-12) Numbers x 30	$ 22.50
(1-20) Numbers x 30	$ 22.50
(1-30) Numbers x 24	$ 36.00
(00-90) Decade Dice x 20	$ 15.00
Operation 4F (+ - x ÷) x 16	$ 12.00
Kit Price	$ 319.75

BONUS!!

> *RECEIVE A BONUS - $34.50 VALUE*

KT-11 DELUXE FRACTION KIT

Piece It Together With Fractions Vol. VIII	
(with 7 fraction dice, one 12-sided number die,	
one mini deck of cards and a 51 piece deluxe	
fraction set)	$ 35.95
16 Sets of Deluxe Fraction Circles, Fraction Dice,	
Cards, 12-sided Dice	$ 284.50
1 Deluxe Overhead Fraction Circle Set	$ 12.00
Overhead Fraction Dice	$ 7.50
Kit Price	$ 339.95

BONUS!!

> *RECEIVE A BONUS OF EXTRA FRACTION DICE - $30.00 VALUE*

CLASSROOM KITS (Continued)

	QUANTITY	TOTAL

KT-12 SUPER SAVER KIT

MATH

			QUANTITY	TOTAL
Box Cars & One-Eyed Jacks Vol. I, II, III, IV, V, IX & version Française		$ 165.70		
Radical Math Millennium Edition Vol. X (with 12 multi-sided dice)		$ 34.95		
Piece It Together With Fractions Vol. VIII (comes with manipulatives)		$ 35.95		
2 Sets of Overhead Cards		$ 20.00		
2 Pairs of Overhead Spotted Dice		$ 15.00		
Money Overheads		$ 5.00		
Large Coin Die		$ 5.00		
1 Special Large Demo Deck and 1 Regular Large Demo Deck		$ 24.00		
3 Pairs of Large Floor Demo Dice		$ 13.50		
30 Decks of Special Mini Cards (0 - 12)		$ 60.00		
12 Packages of Bingo Chips		$ 24.00		
100 Regular Dice		$ 20.00		
Multi-Sided Dice:				
(0-5) Dice x 30		$ 22.50		
(0-9) Spotted x 30		$ 30.00		
(0-9) Numbers x 30		$ 22.50		
(1-12) Numbers x 30		$ 22.50		
(1-20) Numbers x 30		$ 22.50		
(1-30) Numbers x 30		$ 45.00		
(00-90) Decade Dice x 30		$ 22.50		
Operation 4F (+ - x ÷) x 16		$ 12.00		
Manipulite Quiet Dice x 72		$ 27.00		
Solving for "X" Algebra Dice x 14		$ 10.50		
Positive/Negative (1-6) Dice x 14		$ 10.50		
Decimal Dice x 14		$ 10.50		
Money Dice x 14		$ 10.50		
Stratedice Mini Kit x 3		$ 95.85		
3 Packages of Canadian Coins		$ 31.50		
6 Math Packs		$ 36.00		

SPELLING / LANGUAGE

			QUANTITY	TOTAL
On A Roll to Spelling… and More Vol. VI (with 2 alphabet dice)		$ 22.95		
Spelling Rules with These Cool Tools (with two alphabet dice and a set of 60 alphabet tiles)		$ 18.95		
30 Alphabet Dice		$ 60.00		
14 Packages of Alphabet Tiles - set pricing includes 5 upper, 5 lower and 4 blend combo packages		$ 105.00		
1 Set of Overhead Alphabet Tiles		$ 8.95		
Puzzle Island		$ 12.95		
Spelling is the Game booklet set		$ 12.95		
10 Decks of Sight Word Cards		$ 30.00		
Total Retail		$1126.70		
Kit Price		**$ 976.95**		

INCREASED SAVINGS OF $150.00!

KT-16 ALGEBRA FUN "DIE" MENTALS JUNIOR/SENIOR HIGH

			QUANTITY	TOTAL
Solving for "X" Algebra Dice x 20		$ 15.00		
Positive/Negative (1-6) Dice x 20		$ 15.00		
Operation 4F (+ - x ÷) Dice x 20		$ 15.00		
10-Sided (0-9) Dice x 20		$ 15.00		
20-Sided (1-20) Dice x 20		$ 15.00		
Total Retail		$ 75.00		
Kit Price		**$ 65.95**		

SAVE OVER $9

COMES IN A 'HANDY' CARRYING CASE

KT-13 CLASSROOM FUN "DIE" MENTALS PRIMARY K-3 DICE KIT

			QUANTITY	TOTAL
(0-9) Numbers x 16		$ 12.00		
(1-12) Numbers x 16		$ 12.00		
(1-20) Numbers x 16		$ 12.00		
(1-30) Numbers x 8		$ 12.00		
(0-5) Numbers x 4		$ 3.00		
(0-9) Spotted x 4		$ 4.00		
Total Retail		$ 55.00		
Kit Price		**$ 49.95**		

SAVE $5

COMES IN A 'HANDY' CARRYING CASE WITH SOME GAME IDEAS

KT-14 CLASSROOM FUN "DIE" MENTALS MIDDLE GRADES 4-9 DICE KIT

			QUANTITY	TOTAL
(0-9) Numbers x 20		$ 15.00		
(1-12) Numbers x 20		$ 15.00		
(1-20) Numbers x 20		$ 15.00		
(1-30) Numbers x 10		$ 15.00		
Operation 4F (+ - x ÷) x 6		$ 4.50		
Total Retail		$ 64.50		
Kit Price		**$ 59.95**		

SAVE $4

COMES IN A 'HANDY' CARRYING CASE WITH SOME GAME IDEAS

KT-15 FRENCH FAVOURITES KIT

			QUANTITY	TOTAL
Box Cars & One-Eyed Jacks version Française		$ 24.00		
50 Regular Dice		$ 10.00		
10 Decks of Special Mini Cards (0 - 12)		$ 20.00		
Large Floor Demo Dice		$ 4.50		
Overhead Cards		$ 10.00		
Overhead Spotted Dice		$ 7.50		
Multi-Sided Dice:				
(0-9) Numbers x 8		$ 6.00		
(1-12) Numbers x 8		$ 6.00		
(1-20) Numbers x 8		$ 6.00		
Total Retail		$ 94.00		
Kit Price		**$ 90.00**		

SAVE $4

KT-17 DOUBLE DARE YOU CLASSROOM KIT

			QUANTITY	TOTAL
Double Dare You Game Book		$ 10.45		
Regular Double Dice x 30		$ 22.50		
10-Sided (0-9) Double Dice x 20		$ 25.00		
Three-In-A-Cube Dice x 20		$ 25.00		
Total Retail		$ 82.95		
Kit Price		**$ 73.95**		

SAVE $9

COMES IN A 'HANDY' CARRYING CASE

KT-18 LITERACY FUN "DIE" MENTALS ELEMENTARY DICE KIT

			QUANTITY	TOTAL
Alphabet Dice x 16		$ 32.00		
5 W's Question Dice x 16		$ 12.00		
Parts of Speech Dice x 16		$ 12.00		
Total Retail		$ 56.00		
Kit Price		**$ 49.95**		

SAVE OVER $6

COMES IN A 'HANDY' CARRYING CASE

SEND TO:

P.O. # (if applicable) _____

NAME _____

SCHOOL _____

STREET _____

CITY _____

PROVINCE _____ POSTAL CODE _____

SCHOOL TELEPHONE _____

HOME TELEPHONE _____

DATE _____

SUBTOTAL _____

SHIPPING & HANDLING (use appropriate category)

Orders under $100.00: (minimum shipping charge $6.00)   add 12% _____

OR   Orders under $500.00:   add 10% _____

OR   Orders over $500.00:   add 8% _____

SUBTOTAL _____

MINISTRY APPROVED RESOURCES   (#135980407)   **HST 15%** (If Applicable) _____

or **GST 7%** _____

(PRICES SUBJECT TO CHANGE WITHOUT NOTICE)   **TOTAL** _____

Make cheques payable to: Box Cars & One-Eyed Jacks

Please allow 3 - 6 weeks for delivery